TALES OF THE REAL GYPSY

BY PAUL KESTER

GRYPHON BOOKS
ANN ARBOR, MICHIGAN · 1971

This is a facsimile reprint of the
1897 edition published in New York
by Doubleday and McClure Co.

Library of Congress Catalog Card Number 77-142004

Preface

THROUGH the long days, through the hot days, through the days of springtide, of summer and autumn, through the morning and noontide and evening, pass the vans of the dwellers in Summerland, — the vans of the Gypsies.

Through the woods, through the thickets, by pasture and common, down dingle and dell, and through deep cut and glen, by brook and by river, all through the Summerland, over the summer droms travel the Gypsies.

Apray the drom! upon the road! we two shall wander out together, pal, taking the luck that comes, and faring as well as we may. If we miss the patteran now and again, and turn anon into

Preface

lanes that lead nowhere, what matter,
my pal ? For, bethink you, the grass
grows greenest and freshest, and the
shadow of elms falls deepest and coolest,
in green shady summer lanes that lead
nowhere save into the heart of the
Gypsies' land, into the haunts of the
fox and the squirrel.

Like the children of Nature we shall
meet on our travels, we will stray over
the fair country in search of idle adventure and the what-not of pleasant days'
doings that go to make summer days
happy days, long cherished and never
forgotten.

We shall turn backward awhile out
of the hurry and skurry to lounge at
the door of a Gypsy tent, and to gather
the wild-flowers that bloom under the
maples and willows.

The flash of an oriole's wing in the
dusk of the greenwood, the song of a

Preface

thrush in the thicket, the gleam of a
red shawl by the drom's side, the sound
of a child's merry laughter, the scent
of the sweetbrier at dawn, and the sniff
at evening of the smoke from a new-
builded campfire, — these are the things
we shall search for, with light hearts
and gay, you and I, pal, while we jals
on the droms together.

If, perchance, I am but a lazy and
lagging companion, too well pleased
with the sound of the few Gypsy words
that I know and with the sound of my
own voice, why, smile a little, but still
journey with me; for, after all, I may
have my story to tell, and how should I
tell it save in my own way, with my
own words and with those of the Gypsies, and, above all, by taking my own
time to tell it ?

Contents

A ROMMANY GULDO

Tales of the Real Gypsy

A ROMMANY GULDO

I

WE stood at the door of the tent. "Come, dye, be comforted," I said, meaning to soothe her fears. "See how bright the chavi looks. I think he'll soon be fedardar kenaw, better now. I think the worst is over. Has the doctor been here since the morning?"

"No, rye," she answered with the fantastic fear of her people showing in her dark eyes as she watched her child; "he never comes unless you go for him. It's kind of you to do it, and it's thoughtful. But mandy keks that the tawno tickinus, my little child, can't live by the help of the doctor, nor by yours. Oh, my chavi! miri bittu chavi! my Duvel atch pa tumende, my child, my little child, the Lord watch over you."

"Hush, dye, hush. He is waking."

We stood at the door of the tent; before us smouldered the fire, burning a brown circle in the greensward, about us the woods, above us the sky with its amber clouds drifting down to the setting sun. The blue smoke curled up, slowly fading into the sky as the rush of the rippling river faded into the silent woods.

The one van was shabby and old; the tent was patched here and there to keep out the sunshine and rain. There were kettles of copper and brass near the wagon; some harness lay on the turf, old and dusty, much mended by thong and by string. The horses that grazed at a distance were old too and broken. The Gypsies were down on their luck.

In the soft gloom of the tent the child lay stretched on his bed, one little brown hand fallen away from the blankets, resting on the dear old earth that every Rommany chavi — aye, every Rommany chal — loves so fondly. The little brown face in the blankets was worn by the

4

fever; the big black eyes, as **they** opened, were dull with its **heat**.

"Mother!"

"Yes, miri chavi?"

"Is it dark in the tent?"

"It is sunset."

"Is the rye here?"

"Yes, my little pal," I said as I leaned over the bed and placed my hand on the child's heated brow; "yes, my little brother."

"You are always here, rye, when I waken."

"The good Lord sends him to us, miri chavi, speaking our jib and knowing our ways. What could we do but for him?"

And the face which had been so many times the face of an oracle was soft and tear-stained in the dusk of the tan.

"You can't rakker now, mother, can you, since I am so naflo? Oh, mother, if you had seen all I have seen since I lay here, what a lill you could rakker!" The little face lighted up, the dullness

5

died from the eyes, the lips were parted and smiling.

" Mandy 's seen the droms all white as the dogwood flowers, the rivers as yellow and gold as the sun. Oh, the birds sang such gillies, like the sound of the bosh, of the fiddle, at night in the tan! The rinkeno chelikos, the pretty birds! Where 's daddy? "

" Apray the drom, deary, away on the roads."

" Will he come soon? "

" Soon, soon, child."

" To-morrow? "

" To-morrow." As she answered the tears fell on the child's face. Then she bent and kissed her chavi, her rinkeno chavi.

" Where is he? " I asked her, " your husband? You have not told me."

" Staraben apopli, imprisoned again," she made answer softly.

" Ah, is it so! Hard luck, dye, hard luck."

The woman sighed and looked from the door of the tent.

6

A Rommany Guldo

" Here, juckle! here, juckle!" called
the child to a little black dog that had
crept to his bedside. The dog licked
the tiny brown hands that could pat him
but feebly, then crept down in the
blankets, a world of comfort in its
dumb way to the Rommany boy whom
it loves.

As the shadows stretched into the
coming of evening, child and dog fell
asleep, the little black nose by the little
brown ear, cheek to jowl, boon companions, while we sat by the embers
keeping our watch.

Sitting thus in the twilight, with her
shawl drawn about her, the sybil who
had told the past and the future to many
a believer and to many a sceptic was
moved by my questions to tell her own
past to the rye who rakkered her jib and
who knew her ways.

II

" I was born in Berkshire, in England,
rye, of the real old Rommany stock.

My mother was a Stanley, and her
mother a Heron. My father was one
of the Boswells of the west country, —
a prosperous Rommany kral, with many
a pound in his purse and many a gry
grazing apray the common. I had little
enough to envy the Gorgios then. I
was the seventh daughter of the seventh
generation, born with the cloak and
the veil. So the gift came to me nat-
urally, and, as a child, I brought many
a shilling home to the camp that I'd
earned with my dukkerin. For the
most part, we were all very happy wandering up and down the country-side,
telling the great folks their fortunes,
hoaxing the farmers' wives at the
fairs.

"So I grew up with my brothers and
sisters, my pals and my pens, a likely
enough rackli to bring the young krals
to my father's tent, aye, and the young
Gorgios too. But I would have none
of the Gorgios, for, as I told you at
starting, I was of the real old Rommany
foki.

8

A Rommany Guldo

" One day — we were living about Oxford then; what a pleasant country it is of a long quiet summer, though but little to do in the fortune-telling line — one day I had wandered away from the vans and the tents, down the road, through the green hedges, stopping by a little turn where a lane with a gate opened upon the road. I stood with my hands on the bars, looking through at some blue-bells that rocked in the wind, wishing I had them to braid in my hair, when I heard the rattle of wheels at my back, and saw a van come round the turn in the drom, while a man's voice cried out to me as I stood at the gate, looking through at the blue-bells as they tossed in the wind: 'Sarishan miri pen. Latcho divvus.'

" Turning, I saw him riding 't other side of the van and beshing his boshto, sitting his saddle, like any young lord, — as handsome a Rommany kral as you 'd wish to see, aye, or would see, from the first bud of spring 'til the last aster browned in the frost. ' Are you

9

Queenie Boswell?' calls he, a-lifting his hat like a prince of the blood, speaking the Kaulo jib rich and lovely.

"And I answers him quick:

"'What is it to you if I am?'

"Then the old dye who drives the van calls out like any black witch:

"'Tool yer chib, girl, hold your tongue; you were born for each other. Leste's nav's Boswell Heron, your cousin.'

"And so, as you see, rye, from the start we were meant for each other, Boswell Heron and I.

"Often and often my father would sit of an evening smoking his swaggler at the door of the tan, listening while I sang the old Rommany gillies, and Boswell played on his fiddle.

"'He makes the thing talk, does Boswell,' often my father would say, and truly enough. That's why the chavi loves the bosh so well. His daddy could play it so sweetly.

"Can you see the chavi, rye? Is he sleeping quiet and peaceful?"

A Rommany Guldo

"Yes, dye, I can see his face in the light the fire throws in the tent. He is sleeping with his little black pal curled up beside him."

"It is best that he sleeps, rye, you think?"

"Much better, I think. Shall I pile up the fire?"

"There is wood to be burnt, and the leap of the flames is so cheery and hopeful! Dordi! See! the crackle of boughs does one's heart good in the hush of the woods when only the stars and the whip-poor-wills know where the Gypsies are. Let me see the palm of your hand, rye?"

"To pen my dukkerin, to tell my fortune?" I asked.

"No, no. Though I won't give in but I have the gift, if I now and then mixes my meanings, giving the wrong dukkerin to the right party."

"What do you see in the lines of my hand, mother?"

"It says that you have a good heart, and it says that it's many the kind word you've given the Gypsy when he most needed a friend, and it says — "

"What says, my mother?"

"Why the gift, the lines on your vast, the planets, too, and the features. I tells by all."

"By which most, dye? Come, be honest."

"By the features, and by the gift. Did a real Rommany ever lie to you when you asked him straight, and was his friend, and was not prying into his business — when he knew you'd believe him? No, never one."

"No, not one. Unless it might be old Patience Smith."

"Patience Smith! and do you know her? Lord, it's been long since I saw her. A tacho Rommany chie. But I leaves it to you if she counts. She's known up and down the country, wherever a van goes, as an old out and outer, the mother of witches. Dawdy! the habit's so strong on her, she can't tell for her life when she is

12

lying and when she is speaking **tacha-pen**, the truth, if ever she does."

"So you tell by the features?"

"Avali, rye, yes; 't is the easiest way, much the safest. Though the gift comes on me strongly at times, — so strongly that I need but take hold of the hand to pen a true dukkerin. I won't tell you yours. It came into my mind as I thought of the night in the tent, — the camp down in a thicket by the edge of a great wood, — when my mother, Georgiana Boswell, took my hand and told me my fortune, — a thing, as you know, rarely done among the Egyptians in earnest. I had told her that Boswell Heron and I had settled it between us to go our ways in this world together. The fire, flaming up, fell in its red glow all over her face, while her eyes looked back with their flame into the deep of the yog. Sitting so, holding my hand, she said, in a whisper:

"'There's luck in the hand, girl; but it's years and years before you shall reach it; and there's struggle and

13

passion and famine and pain, and a long stony road, a long, weary drom, deary, before you shall reach it. You shall cross the great water, away from the old land that loves you, into the new land that you know nothing of. You shall strive and shall win, but to lose; your children shall die, one by one, and be left by the wayside, before their little hands drop from your leading.'

" ' But the luck, mother? When shall the luck come?' I asked her.

" She sat still in the tent door awhile without speaking, while the flame in her eyes looked into the flame of the yog.

" ' It shall come, miri chavi, when the clouds shall be blackest.'

" ' And the sign, mother,' I asked her, half frightened and trembling, — ' the sign of its coming?'

" ' It shall come without sign, without warning, — as the dawn comes, of itself, in the good time which the Boro Duvel, the Great Lord, shall fix for its coming.'

" So in the face of the evil fortune we were married, Boswell Heron and I, —

14

travelling the old roads of England in our own van, happy as any lord of the manor whose pheasants we snared in the night, free as the wind in the tree-tops, free as the birds in the air.

" The days were long then, but never too long, for they were all full of the scent of the hay and the clover, full of the rush of the rills and the song of the birds that nested in hedge and in dingle, — days when a Rommany's heart goes out of his breast, its last prison, to wander at will over the sweet country. The golden streets that the Gorgios' rashi tells of in his pulpit, where he does all the talking, were not so much to my liking as the green lanes of Berkshire with Boswell, my husband, tramping by the van's side all through the beautiful summer."

" It fared well with you then, dye, — why did you leave the old country?"

" To better our fortunes, as we thought. For the new laws were shutting us out from the commons. We must needs hatch the tan too often by the smoke

15

and the grime of the cities, away from the wild life and freedom. We talked of it much, as letters came from across the great water — talked of it more earnestly as the luck seemed turning against us; our first boy dying just as we thought him safe from the omen, down in the fair Kentish hop-fields, where we had gone with my people for the hop-picking. And so it came about that we made up our minds to leave the puro tem, the old land, for the new country, half hoping the luck would change that was setting against us, glad to go far away from the Kentish fields that knew our first sorrow."

III

SOFTLY the weird shadows stole nearer and nearer, as the flames died out of the fagots. Softly the ashes fell on the gray ashes, striking to the red core where the fire lived. Softly the wind stirred the long grass of the open, moved in the tree-tops, and sighed over the rippling water. The old broken horses struggled up from their sleep to come nearer the tent, standing like gaunt spectres together, at the edge of the circle of light.

"It will storm to-night," the Gypsy said, as she looked up at the clouds, hearing the first moan of the wind, marking how the horses stood listening; "I feel it, and the chill of its coming."

She loosened the shawl from her shoulders, spreading it over the child and the dog, as they slept side by side.

"If the wind changes into the south, it will go round. The storms in this valley come with the west wind and go with the south." But the clouds still came from the westward.

She rose, stretching out her hand to shade her eyes from the glow of the embers, as she peered up at the dark, drifting clouds.

"When the clouds shall be blackest," she muttered, "without sign, without warning, in the time that the Great Lord shall fix for its coming."

Tales of the Real Gypsy

"You think of the dukkerin, dye?"

"I wait for the luck! I wait for the luck!"

The glow of the embers showed her dark face against the black wood, her dark throat without trinket of coral or amber, her worn hands without ring of silver or gold, of roop or of sunakai.

" So we crossed over the great rolling sea, rye, away from our sorrow, to these shores where the van of the Gypsy could roam at its will. A good land it is, too, for tenting; a good land we found it the first year, for we prospered, and the roop and the sunakai, the silver and gold, was plenty enough in our pockets.

" But, rye, we did what no Rommanys ever should do: we bought us a house. In the country it was, with a snug little farm all about us. But you knows our ways, which are not the ways of the Gentiles, and with owning the land came the ill luck again, never to lift till the dukkerin my mother read in my hand shall have come to its end.

A Rommany Guldo

"For with the land came envy, hatred, and hard thoughts, making our hearts heavy and sore, making the days full of sorrow.

"A Gypsy should keep to his own ways, to his own people, rye, if he wishes no ill to come upon him. For his ways are not those of the Gorgios, nor his blood the same blood which the Gorgios feels in his veins. I say, let us keep to the droms by winter, by summer, in chill, in sunshine, in sorrow, in joy — let us keep to the droms and our ways, away from the house of the Gorgios.

"We could not match the craft of the gav mush, the town-man, for our craft is not as the craft of the Gorgios. His smooth jib flowed like the summer wind over the grain-fields; and our guile was as the smile of a child to the coaxing of evil. We fought for our own, rye, as Rommanys should, with vast and with chiv, hand and tongue. But we fought when the fighting was useless.

"I went apray the gav telling fortunes to the town-folk, earning a little; and we held out as long as we could, though year after year the crops failed; for what knew we, being Egyptians and wanderers, of tilling the soil?

"But at last it would not answer. The gav mush, the town-man, the smooth tongue, robbed us of all that we had,— stripped us of vardo and tan, wagon and tent, and left us to bury our second boy in the field where the paupers are laid, bitter-hearted, hating the world and the ways of the Gorgios, the ways that had brought ruin to us.

"Now, Boswell, my husband, brooded of these things, letting the evil grow hot in his heart, hot and fierce, until his hands were laid in violence on our despoiler.

"'T was little enough harm that he did him, seeing that he gave two years of his freedom to pay for the deed, leaving me alone with my baby, the chavi that lies in the tan with the fever. But much harm or little, they sent him to prison; and whether it was easy or hard, I made my way alone until Boswell came back to me when the two years had worn by.

"We wandered away into the country then, and were happy enough. But somehow, never a month slipped away that our van did not pass the door of that farmhouse and by the door of the man who had taken it from us. Then one night we camped at the edge of the town, as Boswell would have it, though I knew it was better we did not; and he left me alone in the tan with the ricklo, while he went apray the gav for no good. So I sat in the door of the tent, looking into the flame of the yog, and crooning a Rommany gillie to quiet the chavi, thinking of the puro tem, the deary old country, of my mother and father, and of the day I saw Boswell, my husband, as I stood by the gate watching the bluebells that rocked in the wind when we were tenting near Oxford. I hung the kettle on the sarshta over the yog, sitting there thinking and dreaming, and watching the slow steam rise, but, through all my thoughts, thinking of Boswell, and knowing that he went apray the gav for no good.

"Maybe I nodded a little, or my thoughts were so far over the fields that they seemed to come back from a dream, when I heard wild sounds in the distance, — shouts that made my heart still to hear. I started to my feet, listened. I heard the furious voices come nearer and nearer. Then I caught up the child from its slumber, and hid it deep in the thicket, out of harm's way, and stood alone, waiting their coming at the door of my tent, as a Rommany queen should stand who feels in her veins the blood of the Stanleys.

"They rushed over the bridge like mad things, rushed up the slope to the camp; they tore down the tan, and rifled the vardo, cursing me fiercely as I stood by my yog in their midst. They swore I was hiding my husband. But I answered them never a word; and the child in the thicket made never a sound, — a

true Gypsy baby. They drove off my
horses; they set fire to the tent and the
wagon; but they left me at last, standing
by the yog and the sarshta, and I had
said never a word.

"Boswell was captured up in the town,
and tried for the murder, done in a
drunken brawl; and, I swear, for he told
me, not done by his hand, though he
hated the gav mush and meant him no
good, — tried and sentenced to prison for
life. There was talk of a pardon, for the
evidence was not all against him. But
what could I do who was friendless and
powerless? What could I do but cry to
my Duvel: Is there no room on the
droms of the world for the vans of the
Gypsies? Must we travel the wastes,
and pasture the gry on the sands of the
desert? Is there no room for the lark
and the linnet, but to fatten the hawk
and the vulture? Give back my husband, — the rom to the romni! I wait for
the luck, miri Duvel! I wait for the
luck!"

IV

"MANDY'S shillero, I am cold, mother. It is dark in the tan. Is the yog all gone out?"

"It has burnt low, miri chavi. The night is the blackest!"

"I am cold, mother, my head whirls; mother, where are you?"

"Here, deary, holding your hand in my hand, with my face close to your face."

"And the rye?"

"Here, miri bittu pal, here, very near you."

"And the juckle, my juckle?"

The dog pushed his nose near the little brown cheek at the words.

"Are you cold, too, my juckle, mandy's nice pretty juckle?"

A hiss in the embers told that the first great raindrop had fallen, and the pale glare, with the low boom and echo, that followed, with the rush of the wind and the surge of the boughs overhead, spoke

24

to the soul of the Gypsy in the wild
language of nature, that none but a
Gypsy can know.

Patter, patter, beat the rain upon the
canvas as it rattled before the wind.
Patter, hiss, and patter, fell the heavy
rain upon the fire, as the storm whirled
up the last sparks that gleamed like
fireflies in the night.

" Mother? "

" Aye, child, what is it? "

" Need I fear the storm, mother?
Hark, how the tan shakes! Do you fear
the storm, mother? "

" Not with the rye here, and the
juckle all snug, and my rinkeno chavi all
safe with his hand held in mine, and my
face close to his. Are you wrapped
from the wind? Are you warm now? "

" I am warm now with your shawl
over the blankets, and the juckle beside
me. I don't fear the storm with you
near me. Oh, mother, mandy thinks
daddy has gone a long way apray the
drom, so far he can never come back to
his chavi, miles upon miles over the

droms and the rivers, where we cannot follow. Though when I dream of the droms that are white as the white dog-wood flowers, of the rivers as yellow and gold as the sun, I follow and follow his patteran from cross-road to cross-road, but never get up with the van. Though I run, mandy runs till he sinks down all in a heap, like the old broken horses that fell by the way in the springtime, and lies panting, and then wakens to catch at your hand, — your hand that is always so near me through all the long night. Will daddy ever come back from the droms to see his sick chavi? Your cheeks are all wet, mother; mandy can feel them all wet with his fingers. Hear the thunder! Hey, daddy! I see your van there by the thicket of hazel. Mandy's found daddy! Hi, daddy! Toss up your rinkeno chavi!"

"Hear him, hear him, rye, — he is naflo again! Oh, my chavi! Is it just that the Great Lord should rob me of him — should snatch him from me in the dark of a wild night, to roam with

the wind over the drenched fields midst
the roll of the thunder? He is all that is
left me. I feel his brow, hot with the
fire of the fever that has borne off his
brothers. He too will leave me, will
follow them over the black seas into the
black lands beyond the black night-
time. He will follow them! And I
shall be left alone in the tan, alone by
the yog, alone on the drom, alone and
forsaken forever!"

"I will go for the drabengro, the
doctor," I said, as I rose from the bedside.

"Out in the storm? In the darkness?"

"Do I not know your ways and
your jib? Should I not then know
the ways of the storm? Trust me to
go safely, to come safe again, and to
come quickly."

"Mother, where has the rye gone?"
I heard the child ask as I paused at the
tent door, "the rye with the soft voice
who called me his pal? Are we alone
in the tan?"

27

" All alone, miri chavi."

" Are you afraid, mother?"

" Not while I have you, and your hand presses mine in the dark. But lie still. Mandy will watch while you sleep; no ill shall happen. For the Boro Duvel has sent us the rye for a friend; and the wind is turned into the south, as I know by the sag it has made in the tan. The storm will blow round to the north over the hills and be gone before morning."

" Do you hear steps, mother?"

" Se kekno adoi; there's nobody there; or it may be the grys by the wagon, keeping their heads from the rain and the wind. Are you resting, my deary?"

" I 'm following daddy again down the drom, where the patteran marks the way."

" Don't roam in the night. Stay here with the juckle and me."

" It is not night on the drom, deary mother. It is gay with the light of the morning, and warm with the sunbeams.

28

A Rommany Guldo

I can see a van, deary mother, that follows our patteran all through the hedges and under the trees where the boughs are so low that they sweep the dust from the top of the vardo as it passes beneath them. And daddy is driving! — my daddy, my kamlo daddy! driving all through the light and the shadow, following our patteran. I can hear the sweet bosh, his fiddle, as it sings to my daddy the old gillies, the old songs. Hark, mother, the wind is blowing them here to us in the night from the sunshine and thickets where the van passes! I hear them! I hear them!"

The black eyes were wide in the darkness, as though they would search out the music.

"Deary mother, you hear it?"

"I hear it, I hear it, my chavi! It's daddy playing a gillie to put you to sleep. Lay your head down on the pillow, sleep, to please daddy, before he has finished the gillie. Sleep, deary chavi."

Slowly the little brown cheek sought

the pillow, slowly the black eyes closed,
slowly the little hand slipped from the
mother's.

"I hear it, I hear it, the rinkeno gillie!
I hear it, I hear it!"

Slowly the light babble of words died
from the lips, and the child slept. Softly
now rocked the wind in the tree-tops;
softly now fell the rain on the tan;
softly, like a distant drum, the thunder
faded over the hills and was gone, and
the pale starlight shone soon where the
lightning had gleamed.

"You hear, dye, the drabengro, the
physician, who came through the storm
says the chavi will live. Let him sleep
out the sleep that shall save him, and
stretch yourself now by his side; for you
need the rest, who have had none for
many a night, while I kindle the fire
with the dry wood from under the
van.

"There's a grey streak apray the
eastern sky which tells that the morning
is coming, and with it the strength and
the health for my pal. I'll fill my pipe

30

now with tobacco, and make a smoke
like the fire in the wet wood until you
shall waken."

V

AND so I smoked by the yog, nod-
ding sleepily over my swaggler, my pipe,
at the door of the tent.

Slowly the warm sun rose out of the
east, stealing up the bright raindrops to
hide in his bosom, sending his yellow
light deep into green thickets, and
glancing over the swollen river. Then
he who had sharp ears might hear the
distant coming of wheels, and the words
of a song, and the last sounds of laughter. And he who had sharp eyes might
catch the gleam of a red dress and the
gaudy paint of a Rommany van down
the drom by the ford of the river.

"Sarishan! Latcho divvus! It's the
Tawno Rye asleep by the tan with his
swaggler on the cushion beside him!"

But I was up and awake in an instant.

"Sarishan!" I made answer, "Latcho

31

divvus! good day! Is it you, Jemmy Lovell? And how is your mother?"

"She will speak for herself, pal; she's driving the third van behind me. Are you out tenting, rye? It's a pleasure to see you."

"Where is Boswell Heron?" called old Mrs. Lovell, driving up in her van. "Why are we stopping?"

"It's the rye, mother. Dordi! You will take a wheel off."

"If I do, it's no wonder, for it's not every day that I meets old friends unexpected; and my sons can't learn to keep to the right of the road."

"Hi, daddy! Hi, daddy! Toss up your chavi! Here, juckle, dance for daddy!"

"Where's Boswell Heron? I've lost his writ, his free paper, his pardon with the governor's name at the bottom. It's under the straw in the van. Beng lell tute! devil take you! can't you help me to find it?"

"He has found his wife there in the tan with his sick chavi. It's a long rak-

ker they'll want before he will have ears
to hear you."

"Off he goes to staraben, to prison
again, if mandy can't find his pardon.
A fine paper, rye, with a print at the
top and a seal at the bottom, — a regular pawnbroker's ticket. And I've lost
it. But never he cares if he's with
Queenie Boswell, his romni. We've followed her patteran many's the mile, and
I never once lost the thing till this moment."

"There it lies under your feet, dye."

"Praise God! Now I have it again I
can look Queenie Boswell straight in
the face, for if he goes back to staraben
it's no fault of mine.

"Out of the vans, all of you! We'll
hatch the tan here to-day, though it's
only three miles we have come in the
morning, — a long three miles for Boswell Heron.

"Thank you, rye, but I don't need
your hand. I'm no fine town-bred lady,
am I? as you knows very well; and
I don't like to think I am getting old.

Jawing the wrong road, eh, rye?" and she laughed as she stepped to the ground from her wagon.

"What! you are not going, my son? You are running away from the thanks. It's an old trick of yours. You will be coming down in the evening to shake hands with Boswell Heron, and hear all about it? Now do. We'll keep supper waiting for you. No? Well, be down before it is over, or I'll send the sheriff to fetch you. He's a dear friend of mine. Don't bring any sweets in your pockets. Well, if you will, for the chavies. Kushto bok, rye! And good luck! And be sure you come down in the evening."

"So that's the Tawno Rye, is it, as I've heard you speak of so often?" a strange Gypsy asked, as I went down the road: "I've heard as how he's written a book on the Egyptians, and made Rommany common, a thing no man ever should do."

"Tool yer chib!" Mrs. Lovell screamed fiercely, "hold your insolent

A Rommany Guldo

tongue. Who are you to talk of your
betters? Sar tacho! He is all right.
Don't I know my own people? Ha!
You are old enough to know better than
to believe all the Gorgios tell you, a-
lying about your own people and turning you against your best friends. I
know his lay — he's a deep one! Dordi!
Why don't you help your wife there
with her tent, while I jaw into the tan
to see Queenie Boswell, and give her
her husband's free papers."

THE HOUSE OF THE GORGIO

THE HOUSE OF THE GORGIO

I

"ARE you camping alone, dye?" I asked as I sat myself down on the cushioned seat that had been removed from the wagon and placed by the door of the tent. "Are you camping alone? or is your rom trading grys up in the town? and where are the chavies?"

"I am camping alone," she made answer, pushing the burning sticks under the kettle with her foot, while with her brown hands she poured the cool spring water into the kettle, where it fell hissing. "I am camping alone. I have neither husband nor children."

I had strayed away from the town, tempted by the breath of the spring and the hazy warmth, by the sense that summer was coming, that it was time to be abroad in field and in lane. I had taken a road that led through the pasture lands east of the town which I knew to be little frequented, thinking only to see the rabbit and squirrel, only to hear the voices of birds as they went about their house-building, with never one thought of my friends the Egyptians.

I knew where the road-people pitched their tents well enough; I knew this was not one of their usual haunts. I paused surprised, therefore, when I saw by a brook, under some trees that were just budding into leaf, backed by a thicket of green hazel bushes, the tent and the van of a Gypsy.

No one was in the tent; but, as I paused at its door, the hazel bushes were thrust aside and a tall Gypsy woman appeared, carrying a pail of spring water.

She paused when she saw me, asking if I had come to have my fortune told. ·But when I made answer, smiling and speaking the Rommany jib, saying I had come to pay her a visit and to gather the

40

news of the roads, and had called her
mother, she put down her pail while we
shook hands quite in the friendly
Rommany fashion.

"You are camping alone?" I
repeated.

"I am camping alone, young man,"
she replied; "I says I have neither
husband or children. With whom then
should I camp, but with myself?"

She seemed not over-pleased with my
question.

"I should think," I said, "you would
camp with some of your own people for
company's sake."

"They wants none of my company,
wants my own people, nor wants I any
of theirs. I does well enough as I
does. You are of the Gorgios, young
man?"

"Who knows?" I answered evasively.

"If you'd been real Rommany chel,
you'd have heard of me. My name's
Phœbe Cooper; I comes of the Lovells."

As she spoke, she turned to her kettle
again.

41

"I have heard of you, Mrs. Cooper," I said.

"Who told you of me?" she asked harshly, never turning away from the kettle.

"I have heard Mrs. Lovell speak of you," I answered, as I arose from my seat. "If I am not welcome, dye, I will go as I came."

I moved to depart.

"Was it Black Katherine Smith, Bill Lovell's wife, who spoke my name in your hearing, young man?"

"It was Mrs. Katherine Lovell," I replied, moving away; "I think she comes of the Smiths."

"Where are you going, young man?" Mrs. Cooper cried, turning about, for I had nearly reached the road now.

"I am going on my way," I answered; for indeed I had not liked her harsh voice and uncivil manner.

"Come back, young man, I meant no offence. I was not thinking of you. It's been many a day since I have heard a word of the Gypsy tongue; many a year

42

since I have been greeted kindly in it, as you were so good as to greet me. Come back and let us be friends."

So I turned back to the tent and sat down again on the wagon-seat, watching the old Gypsy dye as she put the potatoes and meat in the kettle; for the water was now boiling.

"You shall stay and have dinner with me," she said, smiling upon me; "and we will talk of the Egyptians. I shall be glad to have news of them; though they wants none of my company, and I wants none of theirs."

It was easy to see, as we sat talking, that it was true as she had said; that she knew little of her people.

As we gossiped of Egypt the shadows crept round to the north, shortening themselves, and noon came, filling the sky and the day with its warmth and its richness and gladness.

The stew was savory when it came from the kettle; my plate was the cleanest; my cup, of silver handsomely wrought; knife and fork had I also, and

43

they, like the cup, were of silver. But I observed that my hostess was one of the real old-fashioned Romans, for she used neither knife nor fork, preferring her fingers instead.

"The gry is down in the lane nipping the fresh grass," Mrs. Cooper said, in reply to my questions as our dinner progressed. "Let me help you again."

"Thank you. And have you a dog?"

"The juckle is watching the gry, to see that she does not stray, and that no farming engro drives her off; which many would do, if it were not that the dog is so large and so fierce. When I goes into the town penning dukkerin, I ties up the horse to the vardo, and leaves the dog in charge till I comes back from my fortune-telling, and never once have I found anything missing. Though once, not a month ago, when I came home from the gav, I found a tramp in the wagon with his pockets full of my valuables. But it was little matter, for the dog would not let him depart.

"When I came up to the camp, and

sees what was the state of affairs, I puts on my terrible look — and I can be very terrible when I wishes to be — so I puts on my terrible look, and I screams at the tramper till he is glad to empty his pockets of my valuables, with a few of his own; for I made him turn them inside out, nor would I allow him to put anything back. This he does as fast as he can, while I stands glaring at him in a manner to frighten a dozen policemen.

"Now, when I am sure he has nothing of mine, and I sees I have something of his — indeed but small matters, a penknife, a few coppers, a fish-line, and a little tobacco, nothing sufficient to pay for my trouble — seeing this, I calls off the dog, and lets the tramper depart a little way down the road.

"Now, though I bears him no goodwill, I am content enough to let him go quietly, when, like a fool, he must needs arouse me to fury by using foul language, thinking himself safe out of harm's way.

"But he is not safe, ha, not he! for all of a sudden I screams at him, and I

lets the dog fly ; and my beautiful tramper
runs for his life to the first tree, where
he passes the night; for the dog will not
let him come down, nor will I call the
dog off till about noon of the next day,
when I goes on my way, calling my dog,
while the tramper presently gets down
from his tree, with much bad language,
which I pretends not to hear.

"I have heard that my conduct was
not approved by some of my people,
whose ways are much like the ways of
the tramper. They thought I was too
rough in my dealings. But I am one
who cares little for the opinions of my
people ; and I will not be dictated to, nor
will I be bothered by trampers or other
low persons."

"Yours is a valuable dog, Mrs.
Cooper," I ventured.

"You are right, young man, my dog
is a truly valuable dog, and I values him
accordingly, and I grudges him not what
he eats. You will find him as gentle
and playful as any lamb. Were it not
for his great appetite, I could say that no

46

Rommany chie has another such dog in the world, which is saying not a little."

" And his name? "

" I calls him Satan. I hopes you are not laughing, young man; I likes not those of a chaffing disposition. In my day, I have been as chaffing and free as the next. But my day has gone by. And I repeats again, that I likes not chaffing, as it no longer befits my years, nor likewise my character — which is of the settled description. The name is a good name, young man. I finds no fault with it. I am going now to give Satan his dinner, and to see to the horse. If you come with me, you can make their acquaintance."

She arose and led the way along the road, past a clump of tall bushes, beyond which I saw the horse grazing, while a very large dog lay upon the grass watching beside her. The dog was gaunt and coal-black in colour, well-deserving his name. The horse, a large dappled-grey, was plump and round and well cared for.

"I grooms her myself," Mrs. Cooper replied to my question; "I'm a good hand with horses."

At our approach, the dog sprang up to come bounding upon us, while the horse only raised her head for a moment, and then went on cropping the grass.

"Shall you go into the town to tell fortunes this afternoon, dye?" I asked, as we led the horse down to the brook.

"No; I have told fortunes all the winter. And a bad winter and lonely it has been. I shall tell no fortunes to-day, and perhaps none to-morrow. I mean to go fishing. If you wishes, you may come with me, young man; we can talk while we wait for the fish to bite. Do you care to go fishing, or must you go back to the town?"

"It is too clear for the fish to bite well, dye, and I have no skill with the rod; yet I shall be pleased to go fishing, as I need not return to the town until evening. How could I better spend the time than beside a pleasant river in such good company? Have you hooks and lines in the wagon?"

"Thanking you kindly for your civil speeches, I makes answer that I have hooks and lines, also corks and some leads. I needs but a stout rod, which, if you will, you may cut for me."

As we pushed our way through the silvery boughs of the willows, following the brook's side to the point where its current flowed into the river, startling the birds who were building their nests and singing their hearts out for the spring, which they loved, and its freshness and beauty, — as we passed so, over the fallen moss-covered logs in the thicket, over the warm, soft turf of the pastures and meadows, it was pleasant to think there is one race, at least, in the old world who live always in the sunshine and summer.

At last we came to the river, and sat us down under the elms that grow where the brown bank has been washed steep by the current, where the thick green turf hangs out and over its edges, and where the swallows skim and circle, and dip and nest, above the cool flow of the water; and, making ready our rods and our tackle, we baited our hooks, and cast in our lines, and waited.

But I am no great fisherman, and after the minnows had nibbled the bait from my hook a half-dozen times, I threw the rod away, and, winding up the line and the leads, sat lazily watching Mrs. Cooper, who fished with great perseverance, but with no better success than my own.

Though we said little, the Gypsy thinking the sound of our voices would frighten the fish, and I having but little to say, yet the silence between us was friendly; for we seemed not like chance acquaintances, but like those who had known each other for years. This feeling was strong in my mind, when the dye turned to me, as she cast in her line for the twentieth time.

The House of the Gorgio

II

" WHETHER it be the pleasant heat
of the sun, or the pleasant flow of the
water, which it is pleasant to watch, or
the noise of the cawing crows in the
distance, which likewise is pleasant, or
whether it be the sound of the rich
Rommany jib on your lips that has
softened my heart and turned my mind
back to wandering in by-gone times, I
cannot tell. But so it is wandering
now, as yonder crow wings, back slowly
over the long track it has come. But
neither it nor I can fly back to the days
of our youth, save in fancy."

She paused, watching the eddies that
played round the cork as it floated half
out in the river. In a moment she
raised her head to mark the swift flight
of a heron that rose from the reeds near
the opposite shore. When it was lost
to view by a bend in the river, she
spoke again : —

Tales of the Real Gypsy

"I love not the Gorgios, young man, and though you say not you are one of them, yet I think that you are. My years make me over suspicious; but many's the time I have acted the part of the fool in my day, — it will little matter if I act it again.

"You think it strange that I travels alone and apart from my people. It is not my wish that I do so; though I often makes my boast that it is, having some pride yet, and not soon to be cowed, like a Gorgio; but my people will have none of my company, though, as in my day I have told them, many and many's the time that they take up with worse. My people have set their faces against me; they have made me an outcast. I will, therefore, relate for your hearing how it has come to pass that I travels alone for, as I tells you, whether it be the heat of the sun, or the flow of the water, or the cawing crows circling there by the edge of the woods, or the Rommany words on your lips, my thoughts are turned back to the old days, and I will tell you what happened then.

"You are not over-Gorgios, and your conversation shows me that you knows the ways of my people. Therefore you will not wonder at what I tells you."

And indeed the heat of the sun was pleasant, and pleasant, too, was the still flow of the cool water, the caws of quarrelling crows by the wood, the day with its hazy heat and its dreamy suggestions of all that was best in the summers that had been, all that was best and sweetest and most worth remembering. So I clasped my hands round my knee, and lazily listened, with the sense of spring-fever all through my veins, to the tale the dye told me.

" I turns back my mind thirty years, young man, and I comes to much such a spring day as this. I remembers the day very clearly, for it was my birthday; likewise it was the birthday of the young man I had promised to marry. His name was Gilderoy Cooper, and my name was Phœbe Lovell.

53

"I was cousin to tall Bill Lovell, whose family you knows; for Black Katherine Smith is his wife.

"I also remembers the day, because my father brought home to the camp a new van in the morning. I remembers well how we admired it, and not without reason; for, with its gildings and carvings and trimmings and mirrors, it was the finest Rommany van on any road in America at the time I am telling about. We could well afford it, for my father was a rich Egyptian; never a horse passed from his hand to the hand of a Gorgio but that silver and gold stayed in his palm.

"'I will give this 'ere vardo to the first of my daughters who marries,' he said, looking at me; for I was the eldest of my father's nine children, and had long had an understanding with Gilderoy Cooper.

"Twenty tents were pitched in the grove. We were all there, my cousins and kindred, with tall Bill and Black Katherine too, all there admiring the

54

new van that my father had brought home from the gav.

"The chies must needs have the chals to assist them into and out of the vardo, playing at being great ladies, with much light discourse and idle chaffing. And I must needs play the fool like the rest, saying I would have none but a Gorgio for my husband, that I liked not my own people, whose ways were as the ways of the heathen. And I said I would have none for my husband but a beautiful young Gorgio, who should keep me my carriage and pair, and who should have servants and lackeys to run at my bidding.

"Now I said this, though I saw that it cut to Gilderoy Cooper's heart; for he had scarcely a horse of his own, being thriftless and easy and over-honest in all his dealings, even with the Gorgios.

"Seeing that my words hurt him, and being in a wild, reckless mood, knowing, too, that though it was cruel to quarrel, it was sweet to make up,

I let my tongue run as it would, watching his face, meaning to stop when I hurt him too much. Then I said I hated all ugly Romans, and would marry no man unless he were handsome, and not then unless he were rich.

"Now Gilderoy Cooper, though not of a bad countenance, for he had a kind way with him that showed in his face, was yet counted one of the plainest featured among the Egyptians, and had no opinion of his own looks. And when I had said this, I saw him turn away from the chies and the chals by the van; and I knew what I had said had not been well said, and I would have bit off my tongue to recall it. I knew that he was not gone to his own tent, but to roam in the woods. I would have got down then from the van, to follow him and make my peace, as I could have done quickly enough, for Gilderoy loved me, and would cause me no pain for all that I caused him to suffer, but I saw that my father's brow was dark, that he was

56

angered with me for what I had said; and seeing his anger, my heart hardened and would not allow me to follow Gilderoy Cooper into the forest.

" I could scarcely keep the tears from my eyes. For though I sometimes spoke lightly of him, I loved Gilderoy Cooper more than I loved my life or my own people.

" As I sat there on the seat of the van, wondering what I should say to Gilderoy when I met him again, thinking only of this, with the chals and the chies chaffing about me, saying how they would bring me all the handsome Gorgios from out of the town, that I might choose a husband from them, and as my father stood frowning, not liking their discourse, and liking my behaviour still less, then up the drom came a Gorgio — a tall, straight, beautiful Gorgio — and my heart stopped its beating as my eyes saw him, for the dook told me that his fortune and mine travelled the same course, for a way at least, through the world. As he came on carelessly,

slowly, with his fine bearing and fine
face, the chies and the chals whispered
to me that I should tell his fortune
and cross hands with him, and so have
him for my husband. But I said
nothing, sitting on the seat of the van
with my eyes on his handsome face,
waiting.

"As he turned from the road, my father went forward to meet him. Then I
heard him ask, in a listless and careless
way — a way that became him — ask if
there was a witch in the camp who could
tell a fortune. But my father answered
him, not over civil, that no fortunes
were to be had in the camp. He would
have turned away then, had I not cried
out to him from my seat on the van that
I would tell him his fortune.

"So he came to lean on the wheel
of the wagon, smiling gravely as he
gave me his slim hand from which to
read the dukkerin.

"When my father saw this, and saw
the look the young man had for me, he
went into his tent; and the frown on his

brow was the blackest I'd seen for many
a day.

"It was a strange thing to see the white
hand of the handsome Gorgio held in
my brown ones, though the brown ones
were shapely enough in those days. It
was a stranger thing to read the dukkerin on the lines of his palm.

"Never a word said I of what I saw
written there.

"I told him a light fortune, full of the
love of Gorgio ranis, of riches and travel
and long life and all that.

"This I told him, though the lines and
the stars and his features said he should
love but one woman, that he should
never cross seas again, nor live many
years to enjoy his riches. There was
care in his hand, the pain of a great
heart; there was passion and will, with
the spirit to dare; there was gentleness
too and weakness, such as wins pardon
for great faults.

"All the while I was penning the light
dukkerin his eyes were fixed on my face;
all the while I could feel my heart beat-

ing and beating; and I knew that the dook and the lines on his vast spoke the truth.

"He went away at sunset, slowly as he had come, my eyes following him with a kind of charm till the shadows or a turn in the drom hid him from view. Ere then he had turned twice to look back; and he knew that I watched him, though neither made any sign.

"After he had gone, I searched in the tents, in the woods, everywhere, for Gilderoy Cooper, knowing that I should have no peace of mind till I found him, till I had told him what the dook said, and that I loved him and loved no one else. But though I searched well, and searched long, I found no trace of him.

"Then, with the first gloom of evening, to escape the chaffing of the chies and the chals, which had grown hateful to me, I went to my mother's tent; but I could not sleep for thinking of the stranger and of Gilderoy Cooper, and for hearing the laughter and singing of the chals and the chies by the camp-fire.

"When I wakened at dawn, my first thought was of Gilderoy.

"As soon as I could, I crept out from the tent to go over the little hillock back of the tan, thinking to see him grooming his horse by the stream that flowed there; for he was always the first to be about the camp in the morning. But no one was by the water-side, nor Gilderoy nor any other, only the horses, that had gone down of themselves to drink near the shallows, raised their heads slowly to wonder at me and to whinny. I looked from one to another, as I patted my own little pony that came to put its nose in my hand, but his gry was not among them; so I turned back to the camp, sick at heart.

"Then I saw that his tent was gone from its place, and that his wagon was also gone; and I knew he had stolen away in the night, that my light words had sent him.

"I covered my face with my hands, standing so without thinking, only feeling my heart beating within me, only knowing my own folly had brought ruin upon me, and had driven my lover away. I stood there despairing, thinking to fling myself into the stream and so have an end to it all, when my pony again thrust its nose close to my face and whinnied as though it knew of my trouble. I drew its head down to my cheek, whispering to it that I had lost Gilderoy, and that I could never be happy again.

"Then I was glad to creep back to the tent, like a wounded thing, while my heart ached and ached, and the tears were wet on my pillow."

III

I DO not know whether the dye's voice broke, whether or not there were tears in her eyes. I did not look; I tried not to listen, tried only to hear the movement of water and the caw of the quarrelling crows, which still came to us from the distance.

"You will know, young man, how it

was when the camp got astir, and all knew that Gilderoy had gone. It was not easy for me to meet my father's frown, not easy to meet the jeers and the jests of the chals and the chies.

"As I tell you, I had just turned twenty, and my people thought it was time I should marry, my mother before me having married my father at fifteen, the custom among the Egyptians being then, as it still is, to marry early.

"My life was not the happiest in those days, though I hoped, as my father hoped and expected, that Gilderoy would come back. But he did not come. And when the news reached us that he had crossed the great water to England, where some of his people still were, it seemed to me and to my father that he was dead, that we should never see him again; for to cross the wide ocean in those days was more than it is in these days, as you know.

"During all that hard time I had but one friend. That friend was the young Gorgio whose fortune I had told on my birthday. Indeed he was a good friend to me. We met often in town and in country, for we travelled not far that summer; and when we travelled away from the town, he often found business or pleasure to take him where we had settled.

"Trouble came of our friendship; for my father liked him little, and day by day liked him less.

"The Gorgio knew that I was unhappy. He was kinder and gentler to me than to any other; and his kindness and gentleness drew me to him, as the warm sunshine draws the drooped heads of the flowers up till their faces turn to it. It was a bad time for me, and a hard time; and I was not all to blame when I gave my promise to marry him, and kept my promise, and was married to him.

"I have told you that Gilderoy seemed to me as one dead since he had crossed over the water, and no Rommany chal could fill his place in my heart. Neither could I longer abide in my father's tent, by reason of his anger against me, which was a just anger, and of which I makes no complaint.

"And so, as the Gorgio loved me, I went to live in his house as his lawful wife, and my name was never spoken again by my father or mother; for they were of the real old sort, and would gladly have seen me dead and in my grave rather than lawfully married to a Gorgio.

"My husband was rich, and I had the wish I had so wickedly made; for there were servants in plenty, with a carriage and pair always before my door for my pleasure.

"I could not love my husband as I had loved Gilderoy, for he was not one of my own people. But my fondness for him was very great, and I took pride in his proud ways and in his beauty. He was much away from the town where we went to live, — a town where none knew us, — and I was left much alone. I pined in those days for the free life and the wide fields. The town seemed narrow and cramped, full of sickness and death; nor did there seem room to live and to breathe in, for the press of the houses.

"I spoke of this once to my husband. But when I saw that it troubled him, I said no more about it; for as the time passed I grew fonder and fonder of him. I was always gentle with him and loving, for much unhappiness seemed on his mind, and back of the pride in his eyes I sometimes saw sorrow and pain.

"I gave out that I was of the Spanish blood to those whom I met in the town. Like most of my people, I was good at playing a part, and quick to learn languages; and as my husband taught me both Spanish and French, I readily passed for a foreign Gorgio. I played my part well, and my English never betrayed me, for when I choose I can speak it as well as a parson.

"My people never came to my door; if, indeed, they knew where I lived. They would not have spoken against me.

"There was a pleasure in all this; I

66

was counted a great lady, as I should
have been counted, and as I still holds
myself, being of as proud birth as any
Gorgio, coming as I does of the Lovells.
I went to none but the greatest balls.   I
wore none but the richest velvets and
silks, and many fine jewels.   I was not
unpleasant to look upon in those days,
being the comeliest of my father's nine
children; and my husband's proud lips
were prouder as I leaned on his arm.

"But as the dook had said, the time
came when his cheek lost its colour, when
the listless look lingered long on his face,
when his eyes sought mine wistfully,
when his head lay on my breast like a
tired child's.   Then I saw that his health,
it was breaking, and a great terror seized
me, as I thought that a day might come
when he would leave me forever.

"It was terrible for me to see this, for
I had grown to love him as I had loved
Gilderoy Cooper in the old days.   I
cared no longer if he were of the Gor-
gios, for he was my husband; and now
I cared for that alone.

Tales of the Real Gypsy

" I went no more abroad to the great
balls that had been my delight. I would
see no one. I lived only to make my
husband love life, to make him live on
in spite of the dukkerin. But it would
not do. All I could say only brought a
smile — half of pain, half of sorrow —
to play on his lips, where a new sweet-
ness lay.

" He seemed to me like a child then,
and grew nearer to my heart as his
strength failed. He was always gentle
with me, and so patient, never petulant
as he sometimes was with the others,
never once speaking quickly, never once
turning his eyes upon me but in love
and regret.

" In those last days, days that came in
the sweet time of the Indian summer,
when all the forests are flushed and
there is haze in the sky, and the drifting
of clouds seems to have a new meaning,
and the songs of the birds is the clearest
in the murk of the still woodlands, days
when the hot sun burns and the frosts
of the night-time chill, when sunshine

and frost are both welcome, when the
droms and the fields, with the whistle of
quau in the morning are happier homes
for my people than the happiest home
of the Gorgio, — in those days I had no
thought but my husband.   I forgot even
Gilderoy Cooper — even my people.

"Once I said to him, 'Let us take to
the roads, to the free life, let us live in
the fresh air and sunshine.   You will be
strong then, my husband.' But as I
spoke, I knew he was not fit for the
rough ways of my people; while only a
faint smile came to his lips as he called
me a Gypsy and rover, — his Gypsy and
rover, his daughter of Egypt.   And I
bent my head lest I should see his lips
tremble, or the tears that came to his
eyes.

"In those last days, my heart was very
near to the heart of my husband, and I
knew well the depth of his love.

"He went once away; he did not say
for the last time, though I knew the
thought that it would be the last time
preyed on his mind.

"I did not wish him to go; but I saw there was something that called him, that he would know no peace until he had gone, so I stifled the fear in my bosom and said not a word. But all the while he was gone I brooded and brooded. Each day was longer than ten as I sat in my room. I felt then as the lion must feel at the circus when he paces his cage, longing to be with his mate on the desert.

"Then, when I thought I could bear it no more, that the waiting was driving me mad, he came to me like a tired child, with his sweet smile and weakness, — came back to die in my arms, while the last look in his eyes sought mine, and the last word on his lips vowed his love for the Gypsy, his wife."

We sat a long while in silence.

The crows were now done with their cawing, the sun hung low over the west, in the cloudless sky of the late afternoon. The tranquil quiet of springtime was only stirred by the balm of

70

the breeze in the fresh leaves, by the soothing flow of the river.

"And then, dye?" I questioned, shading my eyes as I looked into the west. "And then?"

"My son, it is not easy to tell you. But, since I have told you so much, I will tell you the rest. My husband had another wife in a distant city. He had never loved her, nor had she ever loved him. They had lived apart, hating each other so long that the bitterness in his heart made him think it no wrong to turn from her to me. He had thought me a child; he had pitied, then loved me; he had thought to save me from a life that seemed to him hard, to save me from my father's displeasure. He had loved me truly, and had been a good husband to me; and when these things came to my knowledge, I said nothing, but bowed my head, hiding my grief from the world.

"Then came a day when I gave up all that he had given me, — the gold in the bank, the rows of houses on the streets

of the gav, the fair farms in the country, my velvets and jewels and fine
laces, — gave up all that he had called
mine, willingly, for my own pleasure
and peace, and returned to the droms.

"And my life was as though this I
have told you had been but a dream."

IV

"BUT my own people, when they had
heard my story, drove me away from
their camps, saying that I had never
been the wife of the Gorgio, that she
whom he hated was his only wife, that I
had been tricked and deceived.

"But it mattered little to me what they
said. So I stayed not with my own
people, but camped by the road-side
alone. And when I had told fortunes,
and gathered a little store for myself,
I bought me a tent and a wagon, and
travelled upon my own ways, asking
favours of none, refusing the few that
were offered. And so I went on my

ways, prospering, and if my heart ever hardened, it was not at thought of my husband, but at the thought of my own people.

"Years passed away. Gilderoy Cooper came back from across the great water, came back from England where he had not prospered, and we were married. But even then my family would not own me, and our tan was never pitched near the tans of my people.

"But Gilderoy Cooper, when I told him my story, which I did before we were married, saw it as I saw it, and had never a word to speak in disfavour of him that was dead.

"My life then was like the life of the Gypsies you know, save that Gilderoy was better than most husbands, and that we saw little company. In the winters we went into the great cities, I telling my fortunes, Gilderoy tinkering and mending. I think he never regretted taking me for his wife, and to me the love of my youth returned at the sound of his voice.

73

Tales of the Real Gypsy

"Year by year, the days I had spent
in the house of the Gorgio grew to be
more like a dream; and often and often I
wondered if it were not all my fancy.
Then there were times, too, when I
would waken at night to hear the soft
patter of rain on the tan, times when I
would stretch out my hand to feel the
fresh grass, to be sure that that, too, was
not a dream. I could not tell whether I
was glad or sorry, or sorry or glad. I
think my mind strayed sometimes, remembering my sorrow, missing my
mother's voice more as the years passed,
but only in the night when I would lie
awake thinking it over and over.

"But if one lives much in the open air,
looking much on the green lanes and
blue sky, and hears the ripple of water
all through the night, and pays no
heed to these things, but is a part of
them, one's mind comes back to its
balance as the days go by.

"Perhaps, like my brothers and sisters,
these thoughts would never have come
into my head had I not lived in the

The House of the Gorgio

house of a Gorgio, and so come to think more about life while I lived less.

"Dordi! 'T is late. See where the sun is setting; how yellow the sky is! It's time I had finished the little there is left to tell. Fifteen years ago, Gilderoy Cooper, my husband, died, leaving me to mourn him as few ever are mourned, and to travel alone as I had travelled before he came back from England, — as I expect to travel now till the end of my journey.

"Many Gypsies came to his funeral; but few who came had a word for the wife of him whom they laid in the earth. When it was over, they went upon their own ways; and I, hanging my kettle under my van, likewise went upon mine.

"Since that day my tent has never been pitched by the tent of a Gypsy. And it all comes of my having lived in the house of a Gorgio, whose wife they say I was not, that they will no longer call me sister, but make me an outcast."

We rose, for the sun was indeed setting, and wended our way slowly back to the camp. Now when we listened, we could hear the crows cawing still, but faintly and far in the wood, as they wheeled to their rest in the high branches. One by one we heard the frogs piping from the marsh in the meadows, while the plash of a fish sounded clear as it leaped for a fly from the brook.

All was well in the camp. The great dog stretched himself from his long sleep as we approached, then came bounding upon us in welcome.

I took up the pail and went to the spring for water, for I was thirsty. The draught was cool in the cool of the evening and very refreshing. As I turned back to the camp through the green hazel bushes, I heard the crackle of twigs, and saw the blue smoke wreathe up into the sky over the tent-top and wagon.

"You will stay and take tea with me, young man?" the dye asked as I put the pail down by the fire.

The House of the Gorgio

"No, I must go back to the town now, though I thank you, my mother."

"It is just as well, my son, for as I have caught no fish, I could only make a fresh stew; and, though you did the fare ample justice at noon, you might not have such a taste for it in the evening."

So when I had said latcho ratti, good-night, and kushto bok, good luck, and we had shaken hands, I turned away from the camp to go home by the dusky road I had come in the sunlight and morning.

As I went, slowly the voices of the frogs multiplied in marshlands and meadows, and with each new voice in marsh or in meadow came a new star into the sky.

When I reached my home, the blackbirds were done with their calling, all silent in the dark pine-trees; and every star shone clear in the heavens, so clear and so near that I heard the laughter of children as they stood trying to count on their fingers the planets and worlds that twinkled and gleamed far above them.

When I went again to visit the camp by the road-side, as I did the next day, I missed the tent and the wagon, and only a faint blue smoke arose from the ashes where the fire had been to tell me that Mrs. Cooper was gone on her ways.

MRS. COOPER'S LATER
ADVENTURES

MRS. COOPER'S LATER
ADVENTURES

I

"YOU sees me, young man, in strange company. You sees me, as I sees, with surprise, keeping company with three tramping gentry and four chavies, which latter, as you may see by their faces, having dark complexions and the general look of my people, have nothing to do with the former. You sees this with surprise?"

"With much surprise, mother, for when I last saw you, you were tenting alone with only your dog and the horse for companions."

"You speak truth, my son, as I hope, being of the Gorgios, and having no occasion to do otherwise, you always may. My companions were then but my dog and my horse; now it is different."

6   81

As she spoke she glanced to a tent at the edge of the woods, a tent a little removed from her own, before which three men sprawled on the grass beside a battered hand-organ.

"They were good comrades," I said, following her glance, and letting my own gaze rest on the three tramps. "They were safe comrades, too," I added, as the dog Satan came up to me to put its great black head in my lap and one big black paw on my knee.

"Indeed I finds no fault with their company, as you may see, as I still makes them my comrades. But as they cannot converse in the Romano jib, nor yet in the English, which latter, for good reason, I hear sometimes called plain, I find more entertainment in the company of the four chavies."

"And the three roving gentry?" I questioned.

"Shoon to the gillie Jamie is grinding. I likes much of an evening to hear the thing playing. Often I plays it myself to the children, when Jamie comes home

82

from the gav. Indeed, young man, I still maintains that tramping and roving is but a poor business; yet I will say in their favour that three easier men to manage never took to the life than I have found these here gentry camping with me.

"Jamie was bred to the law, so he tells me; but I doubts if he ever defended a party, notwithstanding the which I asks his legal advice when I pitches my tent within a corporation. He plays the thing with more sweet prettiness than another, therefore his pals call him the minstrel. He also sings a good gillie, and helps me to mind the young chavies.

"The cripple? We calls him George Hunchback. I finds him good at building a fire in the morning, or at lifting a chicken by night, which, though of the Gorgios, you know enough of our ways to believe is an excellent art for a poor person to practise in hard times; and I have many mouths to fill now.

"He is a good man with the horses,

83

too; and the dog and the cat take kindly to him, and being dumb things they tells me no lies, so I trusts to their likes, and I likes him. As you sees, he is uncommonly short, not standing much above four feet in his shoes, while his head is bigger than Jamie's. He sometimes peddles papers of pins, with shoe-laces and buttons, so he tells me; and he carries his basket now, but, as I feels for his condition, I requires very little of him.

"That other? The boro mush with the straw-coloured bal? We calls him Jimmie the Burly, on account of his size. I can find but one thing he can do well, which is to lift the van out of the mire when the horses are stalled. This he can do well; but as it has happened but twice in two fortnights, I puts him, generally speaking, aside as idle and shiftless and of no value; by which you must not think, young man, that I do not value his company, for he is not an unpleasant person, and the chavies takes to him mightily. Therefore I values his

84

company, though I values but little his work, as he does none.

" But as we shall make our camp here for a week at the least, and, as I expect the honour of your company on many occasions, I will make you acquainted with my family."

Rising, we crossed to the tent at the edge of the woods. At our approach the organ ceased playing, the three trampers arose, and stood waiting.

"You have heard me speak of this young man, who is withal a civil and well-mannered person; therefore, when I presents him to you and presents you to him, you will know that I means you are to be pals. I therefore makes you acquainted."

And so it came about that I shook hands with the three tramps in the friendliest way, and sat down on the grass by the much-battered organ, and held conversation with them. As we sat there, four Gypsy children came out from the edge of the woods, where they had been playing, four merry Romans,

and came and stood by us. The oldest
boy was not yet in his tenth year; the
girl, the youngest, was only a baby.

"You sees, young man, the chavies
are of the right sort, real Rommany
babies, tacho Gypsy chavies. Ain't
you, my darlings?"

I noticed a new pride in Mrs. Cooper's
black eyes as she gathered the children
about her.

"Dickey thays I tan't do into th'
tan," lisped little Susia, nestling with her
black curls close to Mrs. Cooper's brown
cheek. "Tan't mandy do into th' tan,
miri dye?"

"She'd be jawing to woodrus before
sunset, she would," spoke up the oldest
boy, Dickey by name.

"I wants to jaw to woodrus, miroko-
kero, I'se tired," said Sydney, the next
in age to little Susia, while Mitchell
cried restlessly: —

"Mandy wants to play with the
juckle! Mandy wants to play with the
juckle!" clapping his hands as he
spoke.

86

" Here, Jamie, put little Susia to bed; and Dickey must let her alone to sleep sound, if it is not yet sunset. Little Sydney shall have his nap, too. Have done with your noise, Mitchell! Dickey, go play with the dog and your brother."

" Mandy don't want to play," Dickey protests. " Mandy 'd rather sit down and listen."

The boy Dickey sits down by my side and begins, with much candour, to rummage my pockets.

" Let the gentleman's pockets alone, can't you! Would you chore sweetmeats without so much as a ' thank you, rye,' of a person who rakkers your own jib? Go away! Your manners put me to shame."

Dickey ran off to join Mitchell by the van, where they shared the sweetmeats he had found in my pockets, and played with good-natured old Satan.

II

THE noon-tide sun poured down upon
the camp, hot as a noon-tide and mid-
summer sun should be. The white
tents shimmered in the light; the fields
lay green and tranquil, bathed in the
warm splendour of the perfect day. The
gay vans, drawn up behind the tents, just
caught the clear shadow of the dusky
wood. O'erhead some slow clouds
moved like lazy kites that boyish hands
were pulling in beyond the dreamy
distance of the eastern hills.

The charm of the summer had lured
me away from the town and its turmoil,
and I spent the hot days in the shade in
my hammock, in a quiet nook in the
country where only the sound of the
church-bells dreamily drifted to me from
the town.

I loitered the days away unregretfully,
and, putting every old proverb that be-
sought industry out of my mind, gave
myself up to the season and drowsy

contentment. When I rambled away from the shadows that sheltered my hammock, it was to find some deeper nook in the forest, some sunnier spot than my lawn, by the side of the river, some odder host than my own, — lazy and idle and listless, my leisure listless and dreamy, and calm as the summer.

Many an hour found me stretched at my ease in the shadow of Gypsy tents, or by the roadside, changing the gossip of Egypt with loungers as lazy as I.

With the coming of spring came the Gypsies; from out of the east and the west, from out of the north and the south, came the vans of the rovers to gladden the highways and byways with camp and with camp-fire, with song and with laughter.

Mrs. Cooper had been first; but there followed so many that I had almost forgotten our meeting when, taking my way down the drom, I came on the strange camp with the tramps and the hand-organ, and found my old friend its mistress.

"Shall you jal to the gav to grind on the organ, Jamie, my pal?" asked Jimmie the Burly, turning to Jamie after some conversation with me.

"None but a fool would stir out in the sun," said George Hunchback, knitting his shaggy brows to keep the glare from his eyes.

"I mean to stay in the shade of the tents until sunset. Go yourself and be sunstruck," answers Jamie, who, I observed, had a good-looking face, with a winning way too, to go with it, and he yawns and lazily stretches himself in the grass.

"Thoughtless as ever," the giant says, with a sigh and a smile. "You will lie all day in the shade, with never a cent in your pocket."

"So I will, pal. For what other reason did I take to the roads? I failed at the law, why should I fail at this too. A tramp is a tramp, not a banker; leave the pennies to those who must count them. Praise God, I am done with those days and am free! Aye, Mrs.

Cooper?— free as a Rommany chal;
freer than he, for I have no tent of my
own, no wife, and no children, and no
man is my master. Let the pockets be
empty! I do not wish to hear the chink
of the dollars again. Maybe I was not
born under a blackberry-bush or a haw-
thorn hedge in the old country; but
I 've the heart of a rover, if I 've not the
blood of the Nile in my veins."

" My son," then spoke Mrs. Cooper,
" it gives me much real satisfaction to
know how you takes to the life. I have
no doubt that some day you 'll be having a Gypsy wife, if you can get one
to your liking, and be travelling the
droms in your own van with your chavies
about you. Which reminds mandy
that tute owes me trin lills in vonger,
in fact, three rinkeno shiners, the which
you long since promised to pay. Take
no offence, for I means none, but I says
merely that if we jaws over the same
droms together, we lives by the Gypsy
law. Therefore we pays our lawful
debts to each other, while we are free

to cheat all outsiders, who may be hocussed for silly Gorgios."

"I'll pay up some of these days, dye, I'll pay up before we part company. But the afternoon is too hot to tramp into the town with the organ, and talking of freedom has taken the feel of the beggar out of my palm."

The light in his dark eyes deepened and changed.

"Oh, miri dye, I sometimes think that the blood of your people runs in my veins, — the black blood, the kaulorat. When the day, like this day, is hot; when the noon-time has stolen the fresh morning dews from the pastures; when the dust is heavy and white on the roads and powders the fennel; when no bird flies in the clear sky, and the heat trembles up from the earth; when never a breath of wind stirs the yellow wheat, and never a cloud throws a shadow; when the clack of the reaper and the slow rumbling train in the valley alone break the peace of the noon-tide: then I lie at my ease under the hedge, with the dog at my side and the dark Gypsy baby, and I say to myself: 'This is better than cities; these green fields about me are sweeter and fairer; this is better, this wild life, this free life — I love it.'"

He laughed as he ceased speaking, abashed somewhat that he had shown us so much of his heart.

Jimmie the Burly sat up, addressing himself to me, as he pointed to his companion.

"You open your eyes and your ears when he speaks. Quite right, for he says many good things I have told him. Now and then, he has a notion or two of his own. But having heard him recite these fine sentiments before, they are a little flat to me now. So I think I'll go grease the wheels of the wagon, for perhaps we may drive into town in the cool of the evening."

The huge fellow arose, with a stretch and a yawn, to cross to the vans under the oaks, where he soon had the wheels

93

spinning merrily to the gay tune he whistled.

Mitchell and Dickey left their rough games with old Satan to go and sit by him. Presently we had all turned to watch the young giant at work.

Mrs. Cooper's voice broke our silence : —

" I would sell my vardo to back Jimmie against any man of his inches at wrestling, or in the prize ring. If he had but the grit for a mill, his mawleys would make him a name. Many's the time I have told him he was wasting his powers; but he has no ambition beyond pleasing his pals.

" You shall know that I, to encourage him in a proper spirit, gets two fine pairs of gloves, which I gives to him as a present, that he may get at the training. And what do I see? What does he with them? Why he taps at the chavies, and makes them as playthings until yeck divvus I sees when I wakes in the morning that the baby, little Susia, has chewed off the thumb of one

94

of the gloves with her danners, and the others go the same way. The burly big giant never will fight. He's soft-hearted like a raku, like a Gentile girl."

"Mrs. Cooper thinks none the worse of my pal for his soft-heartedness. She knows if he doesn't use his fists in the ring, he can use them betimes when need be."

As he spoke, George Hunchback looked off to the van where Jimmie the Burly was turning the wheels in the sun. I noticed that his look lingered long, nor was it withdrawn until Jimmie had caught it, and had shown his white teeth in a smile.

"He's a good fellow," said Jamie.

III

AND so with pleasant talk the day went by and twilight came, and with the twilight came the children round the camp-fire to listen to the stories Jamie told, to listen and to laugh or wonder much, as Gorgios children do.

Tales of the Real Gypsy

Overhead the robins carolled, underfoot the crickets chirped, before us flashed the camp-fire, as the woods and fields grew dusk. All about me the weird faces, ruddy in the wavering light, pressed to hear the tale that Jamie told the chavies.

"This here little Susia, who wants to jal to woodrus in the daytime, but who never wants to go to bed at night, — this here little Rommany rani wants her pal to pen her a story?"

"'Es, pen mandy a rinkeno guldo, a pretty story."

"What shall I tell it about?"

"Pen the guldo all about mandy."

"All about you? Well then: 'Jamie went into the town one day with the organ —'"

"'At ain't about mandy. 'At's about tute. Pen it about mandy, please do?"

"Shoon to the mush, and he'll pen it about you."

"So I will, Mrs. Cooper. Listen, Susia: 'Jamie went into the gav yeck divvus, with the organ to grind out some gillies to loosen the pennies that stick to the gentlemen's pockets. But though poor Jamie played ever so sweetly, the gentlemen all went away, or would give Jamie nothing, or passed by on the other side, or stood on the corner to listen, going off very quickly whenever poor Jamie held out his hat. And poor Jamie was very tired and very hungry, for he had had nothing to eat all the long day.'"

" Miri dye would n't dive Jamie nuffin' to eat? 'Torse miri dye would!"

" Miri dye had forgotten all about Jamie. She did not even know where he was travelling. So poor Jamie was very hungry and very tired, and he sat down on the curbstone, while tears came into his eyes. 'They have all forgotten me,' says he to himself. 'Jamie is getting old, like the organ. Poor Jamie!' So he puts his face into his hands, and cries a little for thinking of the merry old times on the droms with little Susia. Then he says to himself: 'Little Susia is a big girl by this time. I suppose she

7   **97**

never thinks any more of poor Jamie.'
Just as I thinks this, along comes a prastamengro, a policeman, and he trips
up over the organ and falls down upon
it so heavily that the poor organ is
broken in many pieces. Then the prastamengro asks Jamie what he means
by what he has done, and is dragging
him off to the lock-up for doing it,
when who should drive up to the side-
walk, with the horse right across, stopping the way, but Mrs. Cooper, while
the dog Satan catches the prastamengro, the wicked prastamengro, by the
tails of his pretty blue coat. Then
Jamie starts up, looking round all surprised, and there is little Susia waving a
green hazel wand over his head like a
regular witch. Seeing this, what should
the old organ do but pick up its ten
pieces, mend itself quickly, and begin to
play very loud, which so frightens the
wicked prastamengro that he runs off
as fast as he can.

"When poor Jamie has done rubbing
his eyes, he finds himself just like this,

98

by the camp-fire with little Susia on his
knee, — not poor Jamie at all. Now give
me a chumer, and tell me if it's a
rinkeno guldo I've told you?"

"Mandy will kiss you if you will dit
mandy a dreen hazel wand like the one
in the guldo? Will tute get mandy the
dreen hazel wand?"

"To be sure he will," Jimmie the
Burly makes answer. "And if he
can't get one, I will — I'll get it to-
morrow."

"Then mandy will give tute a chumer,
too." And the young lady lavished her
kisses upon them, until finally she was
passed from one to another before she
went off to bed in the tent near at hand.

As I walked home over the dark road
alone, I stopped more than once to
look back at the red camp-fire, wondering how it chanced that the tramps and
the Gypsies were living together.

"To-morrow I must hear all about
it," I said to myself, as I lay in my bed,
looking from the low window close at
my side, watching the old moon rise,

dim and belated, out of the east. "To-morrow, if Mrs. Cooper does not abandon the camp in the night, I shall hear all about it."

And so to sleep and to dreamland, leaving the night to fade into the dawn, leaving the cat-birds to waken the morning, and myself to wake when I pleased.

IV

SUNDAY, with its silence, fell upon the country side, hushing the sound of the reaper, stilling the bustle of farm-life. Over the white roads went the buggies and wagons, beating the dust, bearing their burdens towards the far churches. Away off, the hills were blue in the sunshine, the air was fragrant and fresh with the light wind that came gently out of the west.

"There's a peace that even we feels of a Sunday, — a peace that is neither the peace of the lanes nor the hedges, but that steals over the land when the noise and the din of the town is hushed. I

loves to sit so in the deep shadow with
ᵔ fair bit of drom spread out before me,
while I dreams oᷓ the old times, and
wonder and wonder.

" We are a strange people, rye ; we are
far more mysterious to ourselves than
to the Gorgios who presume to decide
who we are, and to tell us the land that
we came from. How indeed should we
have a land, when we have neither country nor home, we who are wanderers
ever? I have heard of a great stone
head that rises out of a sandy place by
a river in Egypt; if that head could
speak, rye, I think it could tell something of my people. But then, as you
says with much wisdom, if all the mysteries were set right and explained it
would be a bad day for a Gypsy, for
who then would wish a fortune, or give
me a shilling to send them a lover? I
will let it alone, as I sees no good could
come to me or the chavies by knowing
more than we do."

And I thought there is indeed a peace
that steals over the land when the

hearts of all men are atune with a
gentler and holier thought than that of
the busy days when the noise and the din
of the town is unhushed, when the sin
in the world is unchecked by the breath
of gentler and calmer beliefs.

And I too, I thought, with many
another, love to sit in the shadow with
the fair, free road with its beauty leading
away before me, — I and others love to
sit so and dream, too, our dreams of the
old times and the new times, ay, and
to wonder and wonder.

We also are strange people, dye, far
more mysterious to ourselves than to
others. We can all tell you of our
neighbours; but never one of us can tell
his own story. We have heard of the
great stone head that rises silent forever
from the yellow sands of Sahara, from
the shifting sands of the desert. Many
of us have thought in our time, if the
Sphinx would but speak, but it will not.
It will not tell of your people, nor open
its lips to our questions.

Perhaps it is all the wiser for that,

for you know we call the silent wise. If the Sphinx could speak, and could lift, with its long dumb voice, the veil of the mysteries, we might all cry out, begging to be blind again. We might find it a bad day for the Gorgios as well as the Gypsy. It might be we would call many now serious things in our lives, mistakes and delusions, and banish them, as we have banished your people, into forgetfulness, from whence they should come as your people come, dye, to tell us of the old days, of the spells and the charms that held the men's hearts in those times, and which for the moment hold ours with the power as of an echo of words that once held a meaning.

On no other day are the sounds like the sounds that drift out from the town on a hot summer Sunday; on other days the beating of iron in the great foundries, the loud round-house whistles, the ringing of school-bells that echo in truant hearts long after vacation is come, with a hundred lesser sounds, find their way to the green country. But on a hot summer Sunday only the clear church-bells ring over the thickets, only the church-going carts rattle over the droms and the bridges. The white spires rise in the distance above the roofs of the town, and their bells ring and echo, seeming like censers swung before the high altar, sending their sweet notes like a rare fragranc over the woodlands and pastures.

V

"AND so, my son, you would know how it comes I travels no longer alone, and the reason I chooses such company; which, as you now sees for yourself, is by no means bad company?"

"I would indeed, dye. Last night I said to myself, 'To-morrow I will hear all about it, if Mrs. Cooper does n't shift camp in the dawn.'"

"So you shall, my son, I will presently tell you the tale of my late adventures. But I says to you first, that I moves not again so early in the morning, and that I would not have departed so quickly before, had I known you were coming to see me again; which being said, I makes haste to begin my tale by asking you to fill up the cups with the kushto livinor, the good ale, which you so thoughtfully provided."

I filled my cup and the dye's, and the cups which the ready hands of the three roving gentry extended, then leaned back in the shadow to hear the story of Mrs. Cooper's later adventures.

"Shoon amengri, listen to me, and I will relate how it chances we travels together, and telling you so much, I will tell you the rest, that you may know all that has befallen me since I had the pleasure of making your acquaintance on the other side of the town in the spring-time. As you tells me you had hoped to pay me another visit, I gives you my best compliments, and tells you that nothing would have pleased me so much. But the mood seizing me, I hav-

ing been in the camp near a week, I
hitched up my horse and betook myself
to wandering up and down the pretty
country.

"I had travelled a fortnight, or it may
have been three weeks, when one beautiful morning, far in the heart of the
hills, in a lonely country where few of
my people pitch their tents, I saw by
the drom's side the pauno tan of a
Gypsy. The wild rocks of the hillside
crowded it close to the road, while the
thick tangled brambles left me no room
to give it the wide way I gives all my
people in passing. But I turns my head,
and looks not at the tent, and I brisks
up the pace of my gry, meaning to go
by, as it pleases me best to go by the
camps of the Egyptians, when I sees,
without looking, or wishing to see, a
little black baby in the white door of
the tent.

"'Romnichel! Romnichel!' screams
out the tawny.

"Then I hears a low voice in the tan
say, in the Rommany jib, 'The good

Lord has sent them to care for my babies.'

"As I hesitates, not knowing what I should do, three other children come to the tent door, and above their faces I sees the wan face of a tall Gypsy woman, and by the look in her eyes I knows she is dying. Seeing this, I knows well what to do. Therefore I makes no delay, but gets down from the van with all haste, and runs to the woman, catching her up in my arms, for as I reaches her side she falls back, almost fainting.

" I lays her down gently, and I swears to her, by all that I holds sacred, to care for her chavies as though they were mine. She calls them to her then, to kiss them again and again, whispering that they are her rinkeno chavies, her bittu tawnies, her babies, and so dies, laying her tired head down on the poor pillow of straw, before I so much as know from her lips her name, or the names of her children.

"I makes all neat in the little tent,

sending the children to gather the wild-flowers that bloom in the tangle while I pitches my own tan and makes up a fire.

"First, I gives the babies their dinner. Then together we lays the flowers by their dye in the tent. They cry not a little, poor things; and it may be I shed a few tears, remembering my own sorrows. As evening comes on, I puts them to bed in my wagon, out of harm's way, leaving the dog to sleep under the vardo. Then I sits down by the dead to watch the night through.

"I looks sometimes at the quiet face in the dim light. I thinks many thoughts. Maybe I slips from the canvas now and again to creep over the wet grass to hark to the night sounds, to peep into the van that I may know how the babies are sleeping. And if, as I sometimes does, I hears them sob in their sleep, I gathers a few wild-flowers to lay on the still breast and in the still hands, for the fresh dew is upon them, clinging to them like a child's tears.

"I remembers a prayer that I once said long ago, when I jalled to the Gorgios church with my Gorgio husband, a prayer that I'd heard him repeat when he was in sore trouble; so I said it over and over all through the night, as I watched by the dead. When the whippoor-wills called in the morning, and the quails away off in the open fields saw the gray light spread that the woods and the hills shut out from me, then I covered the face with a fine piece of cambric I had, and went out in the road to look up at the fading stars, wondering what it all meant.

"And so the dawn came, and the morning, and the chavies awoke, and it was time I should think what was to be done.

"And now I saw what I had not seen in the care of the yesterday, I saw that there were no vans and no horses, that the tent stood alone, that on the right hand the bushes were broken and the earth fresh cut by the wheels that had recently been there; and beyond I saw where the horses had been tied; for the earth was still rough, and a horse-shoe lay on the grass, but neither van nor horses were in sight anywhere.

"When I sees this, I calls out to the oldest boy, who comes running to me; and I asks him where the van and the horses are? He answers me, Gone. I questions him, only to learn that while the mother lay dying in the little tent she had pitched, up the road comes a party of trampers, who hitches the grys to the vardo and drives off with all that she has in the world, excepting the one little tent, which they wishes to take, but which she defends with her tongue, knowing that it is all that is left to shelter her chavies.

"When I learns this from the oldest boy, I says nothing aloud; but my blood boils within me, and I says to myself, under my breath, — I says, speaking deep Rommany: 'Before a fortnight I shall have that van and those horses. And those trampers shall repent of their evil courses; and they shall remember the day of our meeting.'

"I says nothing more to myself; but I walks down the drom for a ways, till I sees that the tracks of the wheels lead to the westward. Then I goes back to the tent."

VI

"IN the cool of the evening we break camp, driving slowly westward to the first village, which, as it chances, lies about five miles away. There I searches out the Gorgios rashi, the preacher, a Methody in a long black coat, a young man with a kind face. When I finds him, I tells him that I wants to bury the chavies' mother in a churchyard with a prayer over her and a blessing. When I have told him this, he sends for the sexton.

"I makes my camp on the top of the hill just by the churchyard gate, where presently the Methody's pretty young wife comes to watch me from across the road, while I cooks the supper. Seeing that she is timid, I civilly invites her to step over the drom, which she does in her shy way. Soon she is minding the baby for me, which is beginning now to be restless. She speaks but few words, and afterwhile she goes away to her home; when she comes back she brings me a basket, for which I gratefully thanks her, as it is well filled with simple, good food.

"Tears come to her eyes when I tells her of the way the dye died, and the lone little children. She even makes offer to take the youngest to bring up, though she has already three of her own. This I declines, thanking her kindly again.

"It is quite dark when the grave is dug. Some men come with lanterns to lower the body. The children cry their hearts out, throwing in wild-flowers upon the neat box which the Methody brought, and call to her to come back to them in a way that I hope I may never hear again, in this world or in any other.

"The Methody stands quiet a while,
looking down into the grave as he holds
his wife's hand, with his three babies
about him. I stands on the other side
with her chavies, looking down into the
dark place where she lays, as the
Methody looks.

"'Dear Lord,' said the Methody, and
I saw his eyes glisten wet in the light of
the lantern that flared on the top of the
rough heap of earth which the sexton
had thrown on the grass, 'dear Lord,
thou knowest that the life of our sister
who lies here at Thy feet was a life
that knew not the light of Thy truth. O
Lord, out of the night of her darkness,
receive her into the light of Thy day!'

"'Amen,' I heard the rashi's wife
murmur. Then he looks at the chavies,
all crying, then at his own pretty babies
about him; then he looks up into the
night, seeming to see far beyond.

"'The fatherless and the motherless
are Thy charge. And Thy blessing is
with them and with those who befriend
them.'

"'Amen,' I heard the wife say again. Then, 'dust to dust' — and the light earth fell, and the chavies were mine with the blessing.

"I would have kept in the camp by the churchyard, but my mind was full of the thieving tramps; for I had heard news of them twenty miles to the north. So on the next day we left the village and the Methody people, and drove slowly northward.

"Day after day we drove on and on, slowly, for the horse had too heavy a load now. Sometimes I had word of the trampers. Sometimes I lost them again. At one town I was told they had passed that way a few days before, after robbing a poor Italian of his hand-organ, leaving him by the wayside almost dead from their beating.

"A week went by. Soon it was the tenth day. I thought, after all they will get out of the country with what they have stolen; and I almost gave up the search. On the thirteenth day, being overtaken by night, I was forced to camp on a rough ground, across a deep ditch from the drom. After I had put the chavies to bed in the van, I sat down by the yog to have a few puffs of me swaggler, my pipe, just for company's sake.

"The night was very dark and the spot very lonely; the light in my pipe, when the yog burned low, was the only cheerful thing for my eyes to rest on.

"So I sat by the fire, with the dog Satan close by my side, wishing for once that the gav were not quite so far, when faint down the drom I heard in the distance a hand-organ playing.

"I straightened myself up and listened. You may suppose I expected to hear no such music there on that lonely road in the woods.

"It came nearer and nearer.

"I threw some sticks on the camp-fire, then lighted my lantern and placed it beside me.

"Now I heard the clatter of hoofs on the stony road and the rattle of wheels close at hand, along with the loud sound of the organ, and, worst of all, the noisy laughter of drunken men.

"Then the van came into the light of my camp-fire, and halted on the road near the tent.

"If I am sometimes fearful of things unseen, I am seldom fearful of things I can behold with my eyes; so, taking the lantern, I went up to the van, crying, 'Sar'shan,' and asking their purpose.

"My son, when I threw the light of my lantern upon them, I saw they were not Gypsies, but tramps; and I saw, by their five ugly faces peering at me, they were not men to meet alone in the night-time. But, having made my boast, I maintains it, and I says I was not afraid.

"'Hi, there, old lady! Take that light out of our eyes,' speaks up one.

"'Drive on then,' I answers. 'Drive on, if you don't like my light.'

"'Never a step do we go till you gets us our supper,' speaks up another.

"'What's on the menu?' asks he who was grinding the organ, with a broad grin.

"'Drive on,' says I, 'and drive on quickly. I cook no supper for trampers by night or by day, and I holds no conversation with low persons. Kair sig! make a hurry!'

"'Lordy!' spoke up another, poking his ugly head out between the others, 'I've seen this old lady before.'

"'Yes,' I makes answer to him, throwing the light full in his face, 'and you have seen my dog also, which is here with me now.' For I sees he is the same tramper I found in my van and who sat in the tree till the morning. 'I knows you for bad ones.'

"'Drive on,' my pretty tramper says to the others, looking scared in the light of the lantern. 'Drive on. She's a devil!'

"'Not so,' says I; for I sees now they are the thieves who have stolen the grys and the van. 'Not so fast. I claims this here vardo myself, and I wants it.'

"As I speaks, I takes hold of the horses' heads, drawing them half off the road. This tilters the van till out tumbles my tramper, who had leaned over the others, and my dog Satan, who has not forgotten him, sets upon him, forcing him into the glade, where he climbs into a low tree with much loud profanity.

"This angers me greatly; so I seizes the horses close by their heads, and I cramps the van round till it is over-turned in the ditch with the four tram-pers sprawling inside it.

"'Now,' I cries, in the midst of their wicked cursing, 'now will you give me the van you have stolen?'

"'What do you mean,' cries out one from the wagon; 'are you trying to kill us? Come on, pals, let's murder the lady!'

"'Murder!' screams I, putting on my terrible look, with the lantern-light full in my face, so they can see me as they crawls out of the van.

"'Murder!' Ha! I flies at the first, and I cuffs him. Then I flies at the second, who is short, and I cuffs him,

and sends him sprawling; and I flies at
the third, who is very drunk, and I seizes
him by the hair of his head, and drags
him out of the van, and leaves him to
roll in the mud like a pig, while I flies
at the fourth and scratches and tears
at his face and his clothes. Then I
screams and flies at all four of them, and
taking them, as I do, by surprise, I puts
them to rout, driving them back to the
road.

"Dawdy! the fine exercise did my
heart good, once my spirit was up.

"My son, the Gorgios is no match
for Rommany chel, and trampers are
all cowards at heart, saving the three
gentlemen here sitting with us. This
I told to the ruffians in English, as loud
as I could scream it, as they stood on
the other side of the drom.

"The horses took fright at the noise,
and, breaking loose from the van, galloped
away down the drom in the darkness.

"My tramp in the tree called to the
others, for the great dog was biting his
heels in the low crotch. But they paid

no heed to him, standing together whispering and looking at me.

"I sees there is trouble coming, so I runs to the van and pulls out the babies to run and hide in the woods till I calls them again; and they scampers off like young partridges hiding among the dead leaves.

"'Lamb! old lady! Lamb, if you loves your life!' I hears the short tramper cry out, and I turns to see the four crossing the road all together toward me.

"'I runs from no Gorgios, unless it be from the sheriff; nor has I any fear for my life.'

"I then takes up a stout staff, and prepares for whatever may come. Ha! I does so none too quickly, for the four come upon me at once with their fists, so that we have a smart bout, till I levels one with the stick and disables another.

"But it would have been better for me if I had not, for the one that I struck down is up again in a moment, wild with his rage, and coming at me with a long knife in his hand; and I goes to the earth under the blows of the others, my elbow alone left to ward off the murderous villain.

"I thinks that my time is come to jaw pardel the Boro Pani to the Kalo Tem, to go over the Great Water to the Black Land of the Dead; so I screams out for the chavies to run for their lives, for that I am murdered, when, just in time, Jimmie the Burly there runs down from the road with his pals, and knocks over the tramp with the knife, while Jamie and George grapple two others, and I arises rejoicing, and beats off the fourth with my stick, calling to Satan, who chases them over the hill, while my pretty tramper creeps out of the tree in the glade, glad to follow the cowardly brutes, his companions. So they are gone, leaving the vardo behind them.

"I then makes the acquaintance of the three roving gentry who had come to my aid. I thanks them as well as I can for their kindness. But they says it is nothing, saying they were only passing that way in the cool of the evening, and were glad of a little adventure.

" I then invites them to sit down, which they does; while I hunts in the woods for the babies. When I returns with the chavies, I finds Jimmie setting the van on its four wheels again, with George lighting the fire, while Jamie is grinding a tune on the organ the thieves had left in the van.

" ' Will you give us a bite of supper, my lady?' asks Jamie, very politely; and I answers him back very pretty:

" ' Sir, with much pleasure.'

" At which we all laughs, and I knows from the sound of their voices, that I have nothing to fear from the three.

" So we clears up the camp, and I makes a fine stew in the kettle, brewing some tea to go with it, while one fetches the water and another sets out the plates, and we sit down to an excellent supper.

" Now I feels in a very good-humour

for getting the wagon, though my bones ache from the bruises; and I says if I had but the horses, I should wish for no more.

"Then I tells them the tale I have told you just now, of the chavies, only adding, which I did not tell you, that they had neither father nor mother, as they told me their father also was dead.

"Now my new friends, hearing this, tells me most kindly that they will search for the horses at once. But I replies, with my thanks, that as I fears the thieves may return in the night, I desires no more to be left alone till the morning.

"'Well,' says Jamie, 'the turf is as soft here for our bed, the sky makes as cool a coverlet here as the turf and the sky in any fence corner, or by any hayrick. If we are true knights of the road, we will not abandon this noble lady to peril. So, pals, I say, let us stay here for the night. Then we can search for the horses at dawn, before any one is abroad to corral them.'

123

"And so I lays down to sleep in the tent, while the chavies sleep in the van; the gentlemen here making shift to pass the night in the thicket under the bushes.

"And I smiles to myself as I closes my eyes, for I have the van, and it is not yet quite a fortnight."

VII

"EARLY in the morning Jamie jaws apray the droms in search of the grys. All day we expect him. But he does not come back to the camp until evening; even then he brings no horses with him. Notwithstanding this, he knows where they are, for he hears that a farming mush has them tied up in his stable and swears that he bought them.

"So the next day I jaws into the gav to the poknees, the justice, also I goes quietly to visit his lady, that she may know the rights of the matter; and I

sends a writing, which Jamie makes, to the
Methody rashi. Then Jamie, who is bred
to the law, as I tell you before, makes
a nice pretty speech; and the Methody
comes himself, which I considers is
doing much on his part, so that I easily
defeats the farming mush, with my
action-at-law, and takes the horses away
from his stable.

"The Methody comes to my camp,
where he stays over night, as I thinks
his purse is too light for the tavern; and
for his convenience I pitches a large tent
I find in the van, in which, with the gentlemen here, he lacks not for comfort.

"'Mrs. Cooper,' he says to me in the
morning quite early, for he would be
up with the sun to assist me with cooking the breakfast, as he said that he
might not get into bad habits and out
of his good ones when he returned
home to his wife, 'Mrs. Cooper, I observe your singular mode of life with
much interest. I find, too, much subject for thought in the language which
I hear you speak with the children.

May I make bold to ask what you call the sun, which is just rising, in your own language?'

"'Mr. Hickey,' I replied, for such I learned was his name, 'Mr. Hickey, we calls the sun, which is just now rising, the "kam," for we thinks "kam" is a pretty name, and because our people have called it by that name time out of mind. We also calls the trees which throw the long shadows over the tents, "rooks," and the tents themselves, "tans."'

"'I have heard you make use of those words, Mrs. Cooper, and I am pleased to learn their significance. Might I be permitted to further inquire as to the means of your livelihood? As you live in no settled habitation, yet are dependent upon yourself for support, upon what do you subsist?'

"'The arts of the Egyptians are various,' I makes answer; 'for myself, I lives by the telling of fortunes.'

"'But, my good woman,' says he, growing quite serious, 'fortune-telling is but deceiving and lying. It is but humbug and nonsense.'

"'It is very like much of the preaching, I have heard, sir.'

"'Impossible! It is not at all like preaching.'

"'It may be not, sir, for you know best,' I remarks humbly; 'but it has always seemed to me, in the little church-going it has been my good luck to get, that there was a deal of fortune-telling on the part of the rashi, a good deal of promising this to one man and of promising that to another, a good deal of giving the best to our friends and the worst to our enemies, and not a little of crossing the palm with silver for good luck's sake, much as with us and the fortunes we promise. Not that I have observed this in all churches, but in many.'

"He shook his head, saying nothing, sitting a long while apparently thinking. In fact he spoke not again until breakfast. Then he said: —

"'Mrs. Cooper, this is indeed a healthful and excellent life which you lead. The tents are cool to sleep under; the air and the sounds of the night-time soothe one amazingly. The food is wholesome, nor is it unpalatable; while the long days dispose one to thought and are very restful.

"'I wish that Annie, my wife, Mrs. Hickey, could spend a few weeks in your camp with the children. It would do her, it would do them all, much good.'

"'My son,' so I commences my address, 'I travels much up and down the country. I visits many towns, and I crosses many counties; I fords many rivers and I climbs many hills; but wherever my van goes, wherever I pitches my tent, there you and yours are welcome at all times, to go or to come. Whenever I may be near the town where you live, I will take care you know where I am tenting, that your lady with the chavies can come out and make me a visit.

"'It is not often I offers my tent and

my wagon at all times; but when I
offers it as I do now, I means what I
says, and I says what I means, and no
less.'

" 'Thank you,' said the rashi. He
paused a moment, then went on eating
his breakfast. After he had finished, he
put aside his knife and fork slowly,
seeming to have forgotten something;
then, remembering, he repeated a blessing which he had neglected to do when
he sat down, on account, I believe, of
thinking of what I had said of the
preachers.

" In the afternoon he kissed the four
chavies, shook hands with my pals
here, and with me, then went on his
way; and a good man I believe him
to be.

" 'God bless you,' he said to me, as
he held out his hand. 'I shall tell Mrs.
Hickey of your kindness. I thank you
for her.'

" 'Kushto bok, my son, good luck to
you, and remember, my kind respects to
your lady.'

"He went away. Since then we have not seen him again, but have travelled the droms quietly, like one family, these here roving gentry jawing with me wherever I jaws.

"Ha! There, rye, you have the history of all that has chanced since we met in the spring on the other side of the gav.

"And tired am I, too, with the telling; and a fool was I to repeat so much nonsense, on such a hot day, to any Gorgio, even to one who speaks Rommany."

"I will ask you one other question, mother, then I will rest contented."

"Indeed, my son, I will say no more whatsoever, as I am warm, and wishes to rest me in quiet and peace, and to fan myself, for there is no air to breathe, and the beads at my throat seem to choke me."

With which she fanned herself with my broad-brimmed straw hat, as she loosened the corals that circled her throat.

"What do you call a fan in the kaulo jib, dye?" I ventured, bent on getting a new word or two.

"My son, I calls this in my hand a boro stadi; for in truth it is a large hat. But what may be the word in Rommany for a fan, I do not know; a baval engro would come near to it, a wind thing; I remember no other word for it."

"And what may be the name the chavies are known by, — their surname, their last nav? — that is all that I meant to inquire."

"Lee, and a good Gypsy name it is. Their father was one of the Lees of the west counties of England, they tells me. Most of his people are still in the puro tem. But I will say no more on any subject until sunset. Dawdy! I am tired with my talking!"

With which exclamation, good Mrs. Cooper arises and departs to her tent, over which the shadows are falling, and soon the boy Dickey reports that she is sleeping the warm hours away.

MRS. HEARNE'S CHAVIES

MRS. HEARNE'S CHAVIES

I

" BY the God's truth, I say, I never
heard the equal of that. I ask
you, young man, was that right? May
I never tell another lie as long as I live,
if I stays in a tem where the Gorgios
carries it off so high. Here I jaws over
the river into the gav, as who has a
better right than an Egyptian? Here
am I set on by all the little devils in
bare-foot and stockings, by all the dogs
in the town. Now, I says nothing to
that, for have I not my staff to drive
off the juckles and my vast to cuff
the chavies about their ears? Indeed,
have I both my staff and my vast
as they learns to their sorrow. But,
by the God's truth, I will no longer
remain in the land where every chicklo
muskro, every dirty policeman, may
chiv me to staraben for telling a fortune

and asking my lawful pay for the dukkerin."

Mrs. Hearne was, indeed, a tragic
figure as she stood in the dusky room
where the deputy-sheriff, who made the
arrest, had seen her locked safely a half
hour before. She stood near the barred
window, a tall gaunt figure, with the
last gleam of the lingering light of the
yellow sunset gilding her tawny face.

"Dawdy, dawdy! What are the poor
people coming to, when they cannot
take what they can get from the dinello
Gorgios without a gresy muskro putting
them to staraben, to prison, with never
a thought for their children? Here's
the mush with the dud!"

A prison attendant brought in a light.

"It's closing time; you can't stay
much longer," he said. Then locking
the door upon us, he continued his
rounds.

I turned again to the Gypsy.

"You must tell me what has happened, dye, or I can do nothing for you.
It is growing late."

Mrs. Hearne's Chavies

"I will tell you, young man. 'T is growing late of a truth; I can feel the night coming on dark over my heart, for my chavies are all alone in the van across the doyav, the river, and they are young children. They do not know where their mother is. They are waiting for her to come home with their supper. But she cannot come."

"Are they all alone, dye?"

"All alone with the horses. The dog was killed the last fortnight. Ha! he took up some meat a farming mush threw him with some poison upon it. The pitiful Gorgios, they loves nothing the poor person has!

"When the yellow light fades, my chavies will sit in the tan waiting for me, but I will not come. I will not, for the Gorgios are slow to open the doors of their prisons.

"I will tell you, then, quickly, how it befell. My rom, Mushie Hearne, shipped to California in the spring to bring some vans back which his brother left him by will. Coming overland is slow trav-

elling. It's some time before I expects
him. Now I travels with some of my
people, also I travels alone. As you
may know, it is not easy for me to cook
the dinner, to care for the horses, to mind
the chavies, dukker and all. Many's
the day it is little I have to put in the
kettle, or to fry in the pan, aye, many's
the day I have but a crust for my mouth.
But the chavies are fed, and I asks no
more. Now come I to this gav, the
curse of the beng be upon it and upon
me for pitching my tent within sound of
its church-bells. Here do I come to
pen dukkerin; here do I find a foolish
old Gentile who asks me if his son has
not robbed him.

"Knowing it is the way of the Gorgios
for the son to rob father, father to rob
son, I answers that no doubt he has.
Thereon I takes some of the young
man's hair, which the father brings me,
a few threads, and I lays them between
the leaves of a certain book which is
mine, and I says an incantation, boiling
my kettle, walking backward to the

138

water, washing my hands behind my
back, having nothing better to do, for
which silly dealings and the like he gives
me trin lills in vonger, which is none too
much to pay me for being a fool.   The
next day I do the same, and the next.
For each I gets the same luvver; nor
would you do it for less.   If the mush
would make me a fool, he must pay.
Now, on the fourth day I tells him for
sure that his son is a thief, that he has
taken his money.   What does the old
man do then, but ask me to come with
him into the gav that I may show him
where it is hidden.   I makes my excuse,
saying I have my other engagements;
but he will have it that I go.   So I jaws
with him, meaning to give him the slip,
for I likes not his way.   Once we gets
into the gav, I suspects something wrong
by the look in his eye, as well as by his
laying his hand on my arm.   Seeing a
muskro coming toward us, I thinks it is
time I am jawing.   So I shakes off his
hand and hurries away down a lane
to'r'ds the fields.   Now what should the

fool do but set up a great cry and start
after me as fast as he can. I waits for
no more, but, being a good runner, I
mends me my pace, leading him a pretty
chase on down the lane. Ha! Now come
the little boys and the dogs after me
with the mush and the muskro yelling
behind, and the fields and the woods getting nearer and nearer. Dawdy! Then
I catches my foot in a rent in my gad,
and I falls flat in a heap in the gutter,
with a crowd coming up all about me.
The little boys pulling my eases, my
dress, while the juckles snap at my feet.
Then runs up my pretty old Gorgios,
all out of breath; and when he can speak
he calls me a thief for taking his money,
ha! and a mischief-maker for setting him
against his own son. What then does
the muskro? What, indeed, does the
muskro, but take me up rough by the
arm and drag me here for no reason.
Then do I learn that the thieving son
has given the vonger back to his father.
'T is for this that they put me to prison.

"By the God's truth, when my rom

comes back he shall strangle that old man and his son. Bad luck be upon them.'"

"But the money he gave you?"

"Fool that I was to keep it about me. They searched me."

"And found it?"

"May it burn out their pockets! May it pay for the bane which shall be their destruction when their children mixes it in their food! I hates them."

"They have their money again. To-morrow, dye, I promise you shall go back to your chavies."

The attendant returned with the prisoner's supper.

"The sheriff says your time is up. You can come in again in the morning."

"To-morrow, dye, it will be settled in a few hours. Kushto ratti."

"To-morrow." Her voice rang strangely in the lonely place, making me pause in the doorway. "But to-night? My chavies, they are waiting for me in the van pardel the doyav. They are hungry." She turned to the keeper:

141

" Can't a woman go to her children?"
she pleaded.

" No," said the keeper, roughly.

With an oath the Gypsy turned to the
window.

" Have no fear for them, Mrs. Hearne.
They shall be cared for."

I saw her face twitch in the dim light.

" Will you take them this bite of
bread for their supper? They are hungry. I have been gone from the camp
all the day."

She stretched out the poor food in her
gaunt hands.

" No, dye, I'll not take it. But they
shall sup well enough. Make your
mind easy. I'll see to them. Kushto
ratti."

" You've the poor person's blessing,
my son," she called after me as I passed
out through the dim, chilly corridors
into the warm summer night.

Mrs. Hearne's Chavies

II

OVER the hills came the moonlight, fresh with the wind that blew from the west, under the trees shone the street lamps, breaking the shadows with patches of light. Up from the square into the hush of evening floated the faint clatter of traffic, while a carriage rolled silently by over the smooth drive to lose itself soon in the shade of the great elms. Over all the town, peace; over the hills, the moonlight; in the treetops, the robins, hushing their last notes; over the world, the soft wind, the white stars.

My footfall awakened the pleasant echoes as I went on treading the uneven bricks of the pavement, bits of song filled the evening, stealing out from half-opened windows where the breeze gently stirred the white curtains, or, like a benison, ringing richly from the church doors as the congregation gathered for prayer-meeting.

Across the cool square, into the heart

of the town, down the main street and over the bridge, with only a pause here and there to fill a good wicker basket, or to change a word with a friend. So on and so over the bridge — so on to the great elm in the lane where Mrs. Lee and my pal Anselo had once made their camp, so to the van and the tan of my friend in the gloomy room with the barred windows.

I paused at some little distance to put my basket down in the tall grass while I reconnoitred. For all the soft summer night and the lights of the town just over the water the camp had a lonely, desolate look, as a hearth has when the fire burns low and tired children huddle over the coals awaiting the return of their mother. A fire was smouldering out near the tent. From the wagon came the sound of a child's voice, a child singing a child to sleep. The voice trembled. Suddenly the song ceased; the singer's sharp ears had caught the sound of my steps on the path.

Mrs. Hearne's Chavies

"Mammy, mammy!" cried two little voices. In the moonlight I saw three dark little heads crowd to the front of the van.

"Is it you, mammy? Nevader won't go to sleep. I 'se been singing a gillie to he. But it won't shut its eyes."

"Ith 's not mammy," a second voice lispingly whispered; "mandy's atrash, I 'm afraid."

"Mammy?" tremblingly questioned the first voice. "Ain't it you, mammy?"

"Why don't mammy come home from the gav, mandy's atrash," lisped the second voice.

"Mammy? ain't it you, mammy? deary mammy, ain't it you?"

"Sarishan," I cried, coming forward.

"Rommany chel! Rommany chel!" piped the voices. Then the three little heads sunk into the gloom of the wagon and profound silence reigned.

"Sarishan," I repeated, knowing nothing more soothing to the ear of a Gypsy than the old mystic greeting.

"Sar'san," piped a faint, frightened

10   145

voice from the wagon; "but you ain't mammy."

"Tute tan't tum into our tan," lisped the second voice; "mandy's atrash."

"You need not be afraid, pal, for I come from your mother. Get down from the wagon and let's have supper. Mammy can't come home to-night, so I have come to stay with you. Come down and let's be acquainted."

"Who ith you?" asked the lisper.

"I am the man with the supper."

"Where ith the supper?" quoth the lisper, venturing his head a little way out of the wagon. "Mandy tan't dick 'er tupper."

"Dick adovo tucheni adoi, look at that basket there. The supper is in it."

"Ith there much tupper?" demanded the lisper.

"There is enough."

"Ith that all?" plaintively wailed the lisper.

"Do you want more?"

"Yeth, I wanth more," sighed the lisper.

Mrs. Hearne's Chavies

I turned to the smouldering fire, breaking some dead boughs that lay in the
grass into fagots, and flinging them upon
the embers. Soon the flames burst
from the twigs, throwing a merry light
over the camp.

" Now come down, pals, and you shall
see what I have in the basket. Come
now, or I'll be jalling back to the gav."

" Not with 'er tupper? " pleaded the
lisper.

" Come then."

"Us is coming."

They came, first, cautiously descend-
ing, the lisper, closely followed by the
child whom I heard singing when I
approached, the latter bringing the baby,
— three as gaunt little Romans as ever
played by the roadside or begged a
penny for sweetmeats.

" We ith so hungry," wailed the lisper,
pausing by the tongue of the wagon;
"uth hath 'ad nuffin to eat all 'er day."

" 'Sept some cold potatoes," corrected
the child with the baby. " And her,"
tapping the baby's curly head, " her had

147

to have most of them. Jimmie and me
let her eat all her could, 'cause her's
been sick."

"Get the kettle for me, Jimmie," I
said to the lisper. "You shall soon have
some hot tea to warm you. It's a fine
supper we'll have when it's ready."

"Willie'll get 'er kettle," quoth the
lisper, who now seemed to be master of
the situation. "Get 'er kettle, Willie.
I'll poke 'er yog."

In a few moments the kettle hung
on the sarshta over the fire, the steam
slowly curling up into the leaves of the
elm-tree.

I thrust a pronged stick through a
thin piece of bread.

"Will you toast this for me, Jimmie?"
I asked.

"Willie'll toast 'er bread," was the
lisper's response. Then, turning to
Willie, all smiling now in the firelight,
he held out his short little arms.

"Gimme 'er baby, Willie. Now toast
a nice piece for 'er rye." The obedient
Willie toasted the bread, holding his

hand up to keep the glow from his face, while I laid out the supper and looked to the tea, and the lisper busied himself with the baby, which now perched on his tiny knee.

When it was all ready, we gathered close to the improvised table, — the seat of a wagon that had been used as a resting-place by the camp-fire until thus pressed into our service. With the baby now on my knee I did the honours of the simple repast. I found that the baby, despite the cold potatoes with which its brothers generously fed it, still could honour our supper with an appetite worthy of a better occasion.

Warmed by the fire, its hunger appeased, how the Rommany chavi could gurgle and crow, could wink and chuckle and laugh, too, in a most bewildering way.

"Dick 'er chavi," smiled the lisper, lavishly spreading great pieces of butter over his toast with his thumb, while his other hand was lost to the wrist, immersed in the pint cup which held his tea. " Dick 'er chavi, Willie. Her 's blinking her eyth. Ain't her our own pretty sister?"

He withdrew his hand from the tin cup to pat the baby affectionately upon its head, the baby crowing and gurgling all the more, much pleased by her brother's attention, and by the tea that ran down from her curls to the tip of her little dark nose.

" Gu," laughed the baby, throwing her arms around my neck in a fashion truly abandoned.

"What is your name?" Willie, the elder boy, suddenly asked, looking up in my face with a wistful expression.

" You 're not the man that lelled off with the pot of luvver what I 've heard my dad tell about? My dad said he was the pleasantest gentleman what ever he see. Lord, my dad said he had all the money there was in a bank, 'cause he broked open the safe with a crowbar and lelled away with the luvver. Mor 'n the price of a hundred horses, my dad said. You ain't him, are you?"

Mrs. Hearne's Chavies

To my great regret, truth compelled me to make answer that I was not the pleasant gentleman who had lelled off with the pot.

" I can't remember him very well; but my dad said he used to travel with us sometimes when the dirty muskros was a after him. He could rakker, and he gived me sweets and such. Are the muskros after you?"

"I hope not," I said, glancing over my shoulder to hide the smile that came to my lips.

" There ain'th none there," whispered the lisper, to reassure me; " Ith been watching. When Ith seeth the muskros Ith just runned away till Ith got other side 'er big house. Then Ith throwed a stone round the corner, and Ith runned and runned."

Here the baby crowed with delight, and her brothers laughed like merry Romans to think that the lisper had thrown a stone at a policeman.

" Gimme 'er baby," Jimmie begged, well pleased with himself and his prowess.

"My daddy's taller'n you," Willie said, looking me over as he took up the thread of the conversation, "and the muskros been after him. But my dad never minded. He just hitched up the horses faster'n blazes, and drove off like lightning — that's what he said, and they never ketched him at all. Did they, Jimmie?"

"No," Jimmie replied, rolling the baby over on its back while he patted its stomach forgetfully. "They'th never ketched dad."

"I thought you might be the man what lelled off with the pot 'cause he always had sweets in his pockets," Willie remarked, staring at my swollen pockets with longing.

"Ath you got any sweets in 'er pot-ets?" questioned the lisper, new light coming into his eyes.

"Willie, hold 'er baby. Ith think 'er rye ath some sweets in ith potet."

He gave the baby to Willie, and being thus unencumbered and free, crept close to my side with smiles enough to cozen a bushel of sweetmeats from the sternest of grocers.

Soon his tiny hands had rummaged the swollen recesses, bringing forth a little heap, above which the baby crowed and gurgled gleefully, while a deep peace spread over the countenance of the lisper, and Willie's eyes opened wide.

" And you ain't the man what lelled off with the pot, either," Willie repeated in wonder.

" But you ith a pleasant gentleman, anyway," beamed the lisper, " ain't he, Willie? "

"Don't you cheat, Jimmie, and keep all the big pieces," his brother protested, as the lisper made a separate pile of the longest sticks and most desirable chocolates.

" These ith for mammy," said the lisper, clearing himself of the charge and overwhelming me with the sense of his goodness. " We mus' n't forget mammy."

" No," assented Willie, ruefully. " But she won't eat 'em, and you 'll have 'em all yourself to-morrow."

"Ith donth know," sighed the lisper, a shadow crossing his brow, "'er baby may get 'em."

"Why can't mammy come back to-night?" the elder boy asked, his voice trembling a little. The fire had burnt low now, while the hush of the night-time increased with the hours, bringing a feeling of loneliness, too, as the new moon sank to the ridge of the grey western hills.

Then I told them how it was with their mother, cheering them with the thought that they should see her soon in the morning.

"You must jal to woodrus now, pals," I told them, for their little heads bent wearily on their tired shoulders. "Indeed you must go to bed now."

"I ith sleepy," the lisper said, yawning. "But if 'er ain'th nobody to be company for you you'll get lonesome and jaw back to the gav. Put 'er baby to bed, Willie. An' you go to sleep, too; Ith'll be company for 'er rye. You wonth be lonesome with me?" he asked

154

bravely, blinking his eyes to keep back the tears, " You 'ill thay if I sith up ith you?"

"I will sit up, too," Willie said.

"No," said the lisper, still blinking, "take 'er baby to bed, Willie. Ith 'll sith up with 'er rye all alone by myself."

"Go to bed, both of you, pals. Mandy will stay till the morning. Sleep in the tent, or the wagon. I 'll have my blankets here by the fire."

When I had put them to bed in the tent, I spread some blankets I found in the wagon over a pile of fresh straw near the fire, and lay down to watch the embers until they were ashes, then to watch the stars till they faded into the grey of morning.

I had just drawn my blankets around me, thinking the chavies asleep, when, hearing a sound, I turned to the tent door, to behold the lisper advancing to me in the dim light, something outstretched in his hand.

"What is it, pal?"

"Ith your sweth."

155

" My what?" I questioned.

" Your sweth," he repeated, extending some sticks of the candy.

" Ith going to give you half of mammy's; mine and Willie's all gone, an' you ain'th had any."

" Keep it all for your dye, little brother; mandy don't want any sweets."

Even in the dim light I was sure I could see the look of self-sacrifice fade from the face of the lisper, to be replaced by an expression of the deepest contentment.

"You ith a nicer rye than the one what lelled off with the luvver that our dad talks about," he murmured, in sleepy approval, as he retired into the gloom of the tent to his bed and his slumbers.

III

It is well to sleep under a tent in the summer-time, aye, till the heavy hoar frosts whiten the grass in the mornings, it is better than to sleep beneath any

156

roof, and better it is to lie with nothing at all 'twixt one's face and the stars when the night is a clear one and warm.

We live too much in the shadow and limit of our own handiwork, too little in the space and freedom of God's. Like children, we magnify the work of our own hands, thinking we have heaped up a mountain or built us a palace, when, indeed, our mountain is but a dust-pile, our palace but a poor sort of prison.

All night long the fresh wind rustled the leaves on the boughs of the elm-tree above me, all night long the whip-poor-wills called by the river, all night long the pure air gladdened my nostrils till I awakened, refreshed, to see the yellow sun rise over the misty reach of the rich valley.

All the beauty of the night, all its wonderful stillness and rest, which only those know who put by the cares and the comforts of houses, all its peace and its healing had been upon me, soothing the unrest, bringing life back to a truer proportion, giving me strength to awaken glad that a new day had dawned.

"Wash 'er baby's face, Willie," I heard the lisper direct, as I lighted the fire. Presently he came and stood by me, watching the preparations I was making for breakfast, but with a wandering eye.

"When ith mammy tumin' back to her chavies?" he asked. "We wants our mammy. We know she ith lonesome wifout uth."

"She will come soon," I told him, and set him to work to lay out the dishes, while I led the horses down to the creek.

It was pleasant to hear the plash of the river over the ripples, pleasant to see the thirsty animals plunge their noses deep into the swift current, pleasant to startle the birds from their branches and to hear them echo with their voices the voice of the ripples.

When breakfast was over I left my tawny Romans to watch the camp, while I returned to the town.

Mrs. Hearne's Chavies

I roused his honour the mayor from his last slumbers, to hear Mrs. Hearne's story. I told of her lonely condition, of her husband absent in California; I told of her brave little chavies alone in the camp over the river; I pleaded her cause as well as I could.

"Well, well," said the good man, as he buttoned his coat tight up to his chin, "we shall see, we shall see."

But I knew that my cause was won when later, as we went into the sheriff's office, he pinched my arm gently, saying: —

" So you managed to get through the night without keeping the lisper awake. Well, well, to think that you could have dispensed with his company."

" Good-morning, your honour," the sheriff said as we entered his office.

" Good-morning, John," said the mayor, smiling blandly as he held out his case. "Won't you have a cigar?"

" I don't smoke so soon after breakfast," the sheriff said, eyeing the mayor with suspicion, the cigars with that half interest the most indifferent connoisseur must feel at the sight of a good weed.

"Put it in your pocket until you are ready," his honour insists gently, as the sheriff weakens and holds out his hand. Then, after a pause, which gives the sheriff time to sniff the fragrant Havana:

"In the matter of the Gypsy woman, Mrs. Hearne, I think, John, we had better let Mrs. Hearne go back to her children."

"It is just as you please; but, for myself, I believe we should make an example. There are too many Gypsies coming our way this summer."

"It may be so," said the mayor, gently, looking from the window of the sheriff's office across to the barred windows that lighted the jail. "It may be so, John, but I think when we make our example, we will not take a lone woman away from her children. We will take a man, John."

"Oh, it's just as you please," said the sheriff. "You say that's a good cigar you gave me?"

Mrs. Hearne's Chavies

"It comes from Cuba."

The sheriff looked at his watch.

"Well, I guess I can light it."

There was a pause while the sheriff eyed the cigar. Then he rolled it reflectively between his large hands, then he bit off the end, accepting the lighted match I extended with a very gruff "Thank you," accompanied by a look which said plainly enough, "So this is your doing."

For a moment the smoke rose in silence.

"It's a good cigar," said the sheriff. He puffed on. "A very good cigar." A smile dawned upon his lips. It spread to the corners of his mouth, to his cheeks, to his eyes, to his chin. It wrinkled his forehead.

"I never tried a better cigar. I beg your honour's pardon, what was that about Mrs. Hearne? You see, the old man she fleeced is my wife's uncle, and I was expected to do all I could. You see how it is."

"Tell your wife all about it."

And the mayor told the story.

"Why, my boy lisps," smiled the sheriff, letting the ashes fall from his cigar, where they had clung until it was half smoked away.

"My wife says she don't like it; but I tell you it just pleases me better than any other kind of talk. 'Why, you look here,' I say to her, 'he'll get over it long enough before I wish he would. Boys grow up too fast nowadays. You wait and see.' He's a sort of delicate child. I wish you'd take him off with you sometimes on your long walks," turning to me. "He plays too much in the jail yard, I think. He'd be no trouble. Take him out to the Gypsy camps with you. It w'd do him a world of good."

"Now, about Mrs. Hearne," gently remonstrated his honour.

"Why, by noon I guess she can go back to her babies. I'm glad you told me about those children. It'll make it easier at home. But, I say, I think there'd be less occasion for that old fool she played the game on to talk if she'd just pack up and go."

Mrs. Hearne's Chavies

IV

"BY the God's truth, young man," quoth Mrs. Hearne, as we went down the side-street together, "it'll be a fine present I'll make you when I meets you again. And my rom, when he comes back from California, will make you another. I'll be going on to-day, if you think best; but me and my family may be this way before long; I wants to settle my score with that old man; and when we comes you shall know it."

Then on and over the river and down to the lane.

"Mammy? Mammy!" piped the voices. "It's deary mammy!"

"I won't take anything, rye," Mrs. Hearne made answer, as she hitched the horses before the van in which she packed all her belongings. "Mandy don't like the feel of luvver when it comes from the hand of a friend. We shall do well enough. But I thanks you kindly for thinking of it."

To my joy, at this moment a long-delayed grocery wagon turned into the lane.

"Here's a basket for you," the boy told Mrs. Hearne as he handed it out. "Get up, Sally!" he cried to his horse, and, his mission being done, he drove whistling back to the town.

There were tears in Mrs. Hearne's eyes.

"The mayor sent it," I hastened to say. "He told me he would; but I thought he'd forgotten."

"He's a fine gentleman," Mrs. Hearne murmured. "I've seen worse gavs than this after all's said."

"Ith got some sweth for mammy, sweth the rye gave uth. Doth mammy wanth them?" queried the lisper.

"Keep them yourself, deary," Mrs. Hearne answered. "Only give Willie some and some to little sister."

"Ith divide ith," sighed the lisper, with the air of a martyr.

"Good luck, rye," Mrs. Hearne said, as she leaned from the wagon to shake hands. "The chavies will never forget you, nor will their dye. Kushto bok."

Over the grass of the lane for a space, followed a space by the great elm-tree's shadow, then with a tugging of harness, a rattling of kettles and wheels, the van turns out upon the highroad and goes slowly southward, raising a white cloud of dust as it passes away into the heat of the sultry sun.

"Kushto bok," say I as I turn back to the town. "Good luck to Mrs. Hearne and her chavies."

A TALE OF THE ROADS

A TALE OF THE ROADS

I

" IT has been three years since I have
seen him," said Mr. Lovell, the
Tall Bill Lovell of Mrs. Cooper's youth;
" three years and three months, and
I never wish to see him again. He
married my wife's cousin, who was
one of the Whartons, and an ill day
indeed was it for her when she took
him."

Mr. Lovell and I sat on the seat of
the van together, while Mrs. Lovell,
Black Katherine, sat on the floor of the
lace-curtained compartment behind us,
putting her small house in order as we
went slowly over the roads, the first of
the little procession of Gypsies.

" An ill day was it, indeed," quoth
Mrs. Lovell; " for it brought her no

good, but much harm, and in the end it
brought her her death."

We had been speaking of tinkering
in England, of its decline among the
American Gypsies; from that we had
come to speak of tinkers in general,
when Mr. Lovell had spoken of a particular tinker whom he had known.

"Her father, old Grant Wharton,
gave them a great wedding. There was
a brass band to play for them, with a
big table spread under the trees, covered with the most delicate eating, to
feast all who came, Gorgios or Gypsy.
Then there was dancing and singing,
and much wild merriment, Mrs. Lovell,
here, and myself, pal, being as merry
and wild as the next. I played a tune
on my fiddle, the dye sang them a gillie;
all was as if we were well pleased, though
we were not."

"We were not, indeed," quoth Mrs.
Lovell. "I now wish I had lost my
voice before I had sung them any gillies. I wish that the tinkering mush had
burned out his ugly eyes with the sparks

from his anvil before they ever saw Betty
Wharton, who was my own cousin."

Mr. Lovell shook the reins gently,
then, leaning back on the seat, he continued : —

"You see it was this 'ere way, rye.
Old Grant Wharton, old fool that he
was, had taken up with this here wandering tinker for no good reason, except
that he was handy at shoeing a gry or
mending the vardo, if it broke down, or
knocking a tire into place, with other such
matters, and had come to let the tinker
travel with him as one of his family.

"The dye, here, and I never could
fancy the fellow ; but we held our
tongues, for it was no business of ours,
saving that old Wharton's wife was my
wife's mother's sister, and a full blood
relation.

"Once, to be sure, I did say my say
respecting the tinkering mush. But I
got no thanks for my pains. Indeed, I
expected none, Mr. Wharton being a
man to allow no interference.

"The tinker had travelled with them

for a year, and yet they could see no harm in him ; though I never could look in his long, heavy face without thinking he was no man to trust; or hear him speak in his slow lagging way, without catching a tone I disliked.

" Betty had never been one to take up with strange men ; but she took up with that tinker from the very first day that she saw him.

" We were driving through much such a country as this, — through a long valley heavily wooded, with blue hills rising around it, where the streams, swollen by the long rains that came after a drought, were deep and swift and unpleasant to ford with the vans. I remember our van was second, following next to the big Wharton wagon, and that Betty was riding with us, having got down from her father's van just before crossing the stream to see that some kettles were lashed fast to the axle-tree, lest the current wash them away, and had then stepped into our vardo to go over the doyav, the river, with us.

A Tale of the Roads

"Splash went the van ahead into the last flowing pani, and I was turning my horses down to the ford, when a man came from a lane that skirted the river, and called out to us.

"I was for going on and leaving him to the others who followed ; but Betty laid her hands on the reins and would not have it so, and our van stayed where it was, while the others passed us, fording the doyav, and went on on the other side.

"Then I saw that the mush who had hailed us was a young man, and that he wore a kind of harness over his shoulders by which he drew after him a heavy tinker's cart that was quite new, and that was piled high with many small boxes, an anvil, and tinkering tools, with a few pieces of canvas that served as a tent thrown over all. I saw, too, a great dog by his side, — the largest I ever dicked, and the fiercest to look upon.

"When the young man moved forward to us, which he did not do until all the other vans had crossed over, we could see the new harness strain on his shoulders, and we saw that the dog was made fast to the cart by a long chain, and that it pulled also, walking quietly by the side of the tinker, its master.

"'Will you carry me over the ford?' asked the tinker.

"'I don't know,' I answered, 'I don't like the looks of your dog.' Nor, indeed, did I, rye. But I liked the tinker's looks even less. He was turning away with a rough word or two, and I was about speaking to say I'd take him over, when Betty flares up.

"'Pay no heed to the fool who is driving,' she cries to the fellow. And I thought at the time it was rather free language to use of a man in his own van. 'We will take you pardel the pani, you and your dog too.'

"The tinker turned back.

"'What do you say?' he asks, looking at me.

"'I say I will take you over,' I says

to him. I say this as I am a peaceable man, and has no wish to displease Betty Wharton, who is my wife's cousin.

"'But what will you do with your cart? It is too heavy to float.'

"'Let him put his kit, along with the boxes and anvil, into the van; then he can tie the cart on at the back,' says Betty.

"As I make no objection, this is soon done. Then the young man climbs up, standing with Betty, looking out at the back to see how the cart should go over.

"'What will you do with the dog?' I asks.

"'I will let him swim after the wagon,' he answers. And so, indeed, he does, and in this way I carried the tinker over the ford.

"When I stopped on the other side of the river, he unlashed his cart, and, taking his anvil, with the kit and the boxes, out of the van, loaded them again upon the cart, and buckling the harness over his shoulders, snapping the chain

175

to the dog's collar, he followed us down the drom.

"'If you come by our camp, I will give you some kettles to mend,' calls out Betty to him at the turn of the drom.

"He nods his head, but makes no other reply.

"Presently we come up with the other vans ; and about five miles beyond the ford we make our camp on a grassy roadside, near a watering-trough, two hundred yards from an old red brick farmhouse.

"Then Betty goes to her father's tent, and I pitch my own tan, while Mrs. Lovell, here, jaws to the farming ker to tell the farming people their fortunes, to beg what she can, perhaps to pick up a silver spoon to bring home in her pocket.

"While Mrs. Lovell is gone, I hatches the tan, and I builds the yog; putting the kekaubie to boil on the sarshta, and as I do this, with other work there is to be done, leading the horses to water at the trough near the farmhouse, the time passes away, and the tinker comes up the drom as my wife trapses out of the farming ker, and they 'vel up the road together.

"Says he to my wife, as she afterwards tells me, says he: 'Where is the girl who has kettles to mend, the pretty girl who rode in your wagon?'

"Says my wife, as she afterwards tells me, says she, 'The young woman for whom you make such flattering inquiries is in her father's tent, as no doubt are the kettles she said she would give you to mend.'"

"They were my words," I heard Mrs. Lovell murmur; "I recollects and remembers them well."

"These being my wife's words," resumed Mr. Lovell, again shaking the lines, as he pulled the horses into the road, from the middle of which they had strayed to slyly gather a mouthful of grass, — "these being my wife's words, the tinkering man asks her to show him the tent; and my wife shows it to him, pointing it out with her finger."

"And my words were," here interrupted Mrs. Lovell, from her seat on the floor of the little compartment, — "and my words were: 'Follow the road till you reach the last tent on your left, and that will be the tent where you shall find the young woman, the pretty young woman who has kettles to mend.' Then I pointed to Grant Wharton's tan with my finger, and those were my words and expressions."

Here Mr. Lovell resumed the recital, Mrs. Lovell resuming her almost habitual silence.

"These being my wife's words and expressions, the tinker passed on to the tent, where we presently sees him sitting upon the grass, mending an old broken kettle, while Mr. Wharton looks on, and Betty sits in the tent-door, petting the tinker's great dog.

"In the evening he spreads his pieces of canvas over the fence where, with his boro juckle, his great dog, he passes the night, his cart drawn up near at hand.

A Tale of the Roads

"When morning comes, I expect to see him jal on the drom. But not so. He stays to mend more broken metal and to tinker a wagon for Betty's father. The morning passes away, the afternoon and the evening, and another night; the work is slow; it is many days before it is finished, and by that time the tinker is one of the Whartons, living in their tents, cooking at their fire, riding with them sometimes in their great van; though for the most part he walks in the road, dragging his cart, with the dog pulling beside him."

II

"Now Mrs. Lovell, here, my wife, who has a quick eye in her head, comes to me one day, saying: If she is not deceived, that there tinkering mush is making up to Betty Wharton. And before long, sure enough, it is known among the Egyptians that they are to be married."

"And my words were," vouchsafed Mrs. Lovell, "'it will be an ill day for Betty Wharton when she goes to live in the tinker's tent as his lawful wife,'—such were my words, and I do not gainsay them now."

We drove on in silence for a little while, passing between some beautiful corn-fields that spread over the rich bottom lands of the valley. Then Mr. Lovell continued the story:—

"We observed, Mrs. Lovell and I, that the tinker's wooing was a rough one. Not a few times we found pretty Betty with tears in her black eyes. But she made no complaint, and only was angry when we begged her to give up her tinker, to marry a real Rommany chal, as a Rommany chie should do. But, as I say, she only grew angry, and our persuading did not prevail.

"Then came the wedding, with the great feast and the brass-band and all. As I tells you, Mrs. Lovell and I were as merry and wild as the next, until it

was over and the tinker and Betty had
gone on their way with a van and two
grys that her father had given her as a
dowry. For a time, we heard nothing
of them; and when we did hear, a month
after the wedding, from some of our
people who had met them and travelled
a day's journey with them, we heard
nothing but good. And so for some
six months or more. Then it changed.
My wife, here, and I met them one
evening standing alone together by the
roadside at sunset, with only the cart
and the dog, with the pieces of canvas
stretched over the fence in the place of
their tent.

" ' They were down on their luck,'
said the tinker, and told a long story as
how he had found his wife Betty taken
with a fever, as how things had turned
against them, the van and the grys
going in their hard times for doctors
and drugs and such nonsense. To prove
what he said, as a liar always wishes to
do, he turned to his wife, who, indeed,
looked not able to stand; and she smiled

in his face very gently, saying it was all true.

"We made our own camp by theirs; and I sat down by Betty's husband, while he beat out some iron on his anvil, and I spoke to him as well as I could for the sound of the blows, giving him some good advice about horse-trading, wishing to help him along, and promising to lend him a hand — perhaps to give him a gry from my own drove, if need be, to start him again. As I spoke, he seemed pleasant enough in his surly way, though scant with his thanks, as he always had been; and I felt much inclined to be friendly, when, as I sat there, the dye, here, came up to my side, tweaking at my sleeve, and I presently rose and followed her into our tent.

"'You fool,' says my wife, 'beng lell tute, devil take you! You are as green as a Gorgios! I knew from the first the fellow was lying, and now I know it for certain.'

"'I believe he speaks tacho —' I was beginning.

182

A Tale of the Roads

"'He speaks lies,' says my wife; 'and hold your tongue or speak low lest he hear you.'

"'There's nobody listening,' I answers; 'do you fear your own shadow?'

"'I fear him, for I know of his deeds,' says my wife."

"Those were my words," assented Mrs. Lovell, "'I fear him for I know of his deeds,' as I did; and when I had made my rom, here, speak low, I told him what I had seen. And now he may tell you."

"My wife had gone to talk with Betty while I sat on the grass near the tinker, to ask her about her sickness. Now my wife saw as she talked that there were dark bruises on Betty's thin arms, dark scars on her forehead and throat; and though my wife said nothing of this, she knew well what it meant. She saw, too, that Betty's shoulders were grown round, that her breast was hollow and shrunken; and though she said nothing of this she knew well what it meant, as I knew when I heard it.

" That evening the tinker went into the town. When he returned, late at night, we could hear him cursing his wife in the low tent by the fence, and we could hear her soft voice as she tried to quiet his ravings.

" I said to my wife, I said, the tinker is drunk; and my wife said to me, it is true, he is drunk like a beast, and furthermore my wife said she knew he had sold the van and the grys for his own pleasure, squandering the money he got in riot and drinking. This we afterward learned was the truth.

" ' You shall give him no gry,' said my wife, ' no horse to sell cheap for his low pleasures.'

" So we lay awake, talking in whispers, all the while hearing Betty's soft voice answer the tinker's rough curses. It was dawn when Mrs. Lovell, here, awoke me.

" The tinker had but then fallen asleep, so she said; we could still hear Betty weeping.

" ' You may give them the gry, if it

184

pleases your fancy,' says my wife, ' and I will give her some clothes for her back, and some advice for her head, for I pities her sorely.'

" When the time came, I gave him the gry with a little light wagon I had ; and my wife she gave Betty all she could spare of her eases, her clothes. Then we shook hands and left them, and glad and sorry, and sorry and glad were we to part from their company. Glad to get free of the drinking and cursing, and Betty's sad eyes, — sorry to leave her, where she would stay by his side.

" We heard from some of our people that the gry and the wagon soon followed the others, that the tinker was very poor. Now I could well enough do without the gry, nor did I much miss the wagon, neither am I one to press any of my people who may be pazorhus to me, though I myself am never pazorhus — indebted — to any man save the Gorgios, who I find no necessity to trouble about; but I liked not the thought that the tinker had sold the gry cheap for his pleasures, and I vows I will help him no more.

"Maybe another six months go by, we hearing nothing from them; and another six months with only rumours of them coming up from the south. So they pass from our minds, and we nearly forget them."

"And then, pal?" I asked Mr. Lovell.

"Well, we travel and travel, hearing, as I say, nothing or little of them, and we almost forget them; though I now and then remembers the gry and the little light wagon, wishing I had them again, that they had not gone for his pleasures; and so the time passes pleasantly by for the most part till ône day, as we jogs over the droms, my wife, here, lays her hand on my hand, as I holds the reins loosely, saying to me, using her own words, that if I look I may see the patteran mark of some of our people there on the roadside. I looked, pal. There, sure enough, was a cross drawn in the dust, with the long end pointing down the road the Gypsies had taken.

"Having no special business in the town where we were going, we turned us aside into the drom which the patteran marked; sure to come up with some of our own kind, if not with friends or relations. As we went on and on, at every cross-roads was the patteran mark, the long point of the cross showing us the drom the Gypsies had taken.

"'The finger that drew that line in the dust is a child's finger or a woman's,' at last says my wife, as we halt at a point in the fields where a track crosses ours, to make sure of the way, as the evening is coming.

"I then gets down from my seat on the van to examine the trail we had followed. And, indeed, I can see that it was drawn by a woman, for the furrow which runs through the sand is narrow and smooth, showing 't was a small finger that made it; firm and straight,

showing that it was no child's work.
It was freshly made, too.

" 'Wiflekin,' I say to Mrs. Lovell,
here, as I looks all about me, 'wifle-
ken, we have been fools.' "

" Those were his words," quoth Mrs.
Lovell in her deep voice from behind.

" 'Wiflekin,' I say again, 'we are
dinello, we are fools. Where are the
tracks of the wheels? Where are the
marks of the horses? Wiflekin, we are
indeed dinello.'

" 'To be sure,' answers my wife, 'we
are dinello. Where, indeed, are the
marks of the hoofs and the wheels?'
And she gets down into the road and
stands beside me.

" 'Is this the trick of a Gorgios ricklo,
a Gentile boy, who would cheat us?'

" 'What knows the Gorgios ricklos of
the patteran? It is the mark of one of
our own people, — the mark of a tacho
Rommany chie.'

" When she had said this, my wife
walks back the road a little way, looking at it ; then she returns to me and

goes on down the drom, for it may be
fifty yards, then, suddenly turning, she
screams out to me, and I leave the van
where it is and run to her quickly, for
I see she has found what it is.

"My wife says nothing, for she is not
one to use many words except when
telling a fortune, but she points to some
tracks in the dust on the drom, and I
see what she has seen and I know what
she knows. First, I see the narrow,
deep furrows the two wheels of a heavy
cart have cut — they are closer together
than the wheels of a wagon should be;
then I see the print of a woman's foot
in the dust, and near it the round mottled spot where a dog's foot has been.

"'It is Betty,' my wife says.

"And I say to my wife: —

"'Let us drive on.'

"And she says to me: —

"'We follow the patteran?'

"And I say to her: —

"'Wiflekin, we do.'

"So we goes on at a good pace, — it
may be a mile, — when at the edge of

the woods we see a woman drawing a
cart, with a great dog straining beside
her. We call out to her, and she stops
at the edge of the woods, waiting for us
to come up; and when we come nearer,
we see it is Betty, and she sees who it
is that has called out to her."

III

" I HOPE while I live, pal, I may never
see another of my people so broken and
changed as Betty was. Her pretty
black hair was all matted; there were
wide streaks of grey in its tangle; and
grey hair, as you know, is but little seen
even among our oldest women. Her
cheeks and her eyes were sunken and
hollow, and her face was as pale and as
bleached as a Gorgios'. The heavy
harness cut into her shoulders and
breast till, I saw, she had slipped her
hands up under the buckles, palms out-
ward, to cover her bosom. Lord!
Lord! rye, it was awful to look upon.
" I drew up the horses on the road-

side at the edge of the woods. Mrs. Lovell, here, got down quickly, striping off the harness from Betty's shoulders. Then they sat together on the side of the cart, with their arms about each other, crying and crying.

" But no hard word said Betty of the tinker, her husband.

"We made our camp where we had halted, though there was neither water nor grass for the horses, and managed to put through the night waiting for the tinker to come up with us. He had stayed behind in the village to get his pay for some work he had done, Betty told us; though we well knew he had stayed for worse reasons; she had come on alone with the cart, the dog doing nearly all the pulling, she said, to get to a town over the hills where there was much mending to do. She could tinker a little herself, now, she told us, — he had taught her to do it; and she turned her hand to that when there were no fortunes to tell. She had left the patteran trail that he might know

191

the way she had come, and so overtake her.

"It was a sad story, full of a woman's lying that did not deceive, and a woman's laughter and tears.

"We stayed there two days before the tinker came up with us; and for those days I had to lead the horses a long way to water, and to let down the rails that they might eat the young wheat in the night-time, else they would have had nothing to feed upon.

"When the tinker comes up with us, at last, we are glad to break camp and travel on to the nearest town, that we may have others about us, for the tinker is not a pleasant companion. He is sullen and surly. He makes no excuses when he harnesses his young wife side by side with the dog to the cart. He carries a heavy staff in his hand as he slouches behind them. I wonder if he ever strikes the girl with it as he strikes the great dog. But she makes no complaint, nor will she let us make any.

"'It will do no good,' is all that she

says. And we see that it will not, so long as she stays with him. And she says she will stay by his side to the end.

"'Tool yer chib! Hold your tongue!' is all the answer I get from the tinker himself when I speak to him of this; and as he curses his wife in the evening for nothing at all but a loving caress, I see I must leave them alone, for that what I say does no good, and even does harm.

"So the dye, here, tells some fortunes, and I putch some grys with the horse traders, while the tinker works at his kettles in our camp on the common just out of the town, and Betty has some pleasanter days, and things go on better with them.

"The tinker keeps well at his work, and, when sober, seems fond of his wife in his rough way. Indeed, seeing this, we grow to think better of him, though it is hard to forget what we know.

"We had been in our camp on the

common three weeks, when one day I goes into the town with some horses to trade on the square. It was a good day for me, as I passed off some of my worst horses for the Gorgios' good money, and was hoping to sell all the old ones before evening. I had just gone into a bar for a drop of beer with a mush who was slow at deciding, and had just put down my shiner to pay for the lovinor, when I see my wife beckoning to me from the door.

"So I drink down the beer at a swallow, and pocket my change, and am just asking her why she left the camp to come into the town to tell fortunes, leaving only Betty to care for our wagon, — for I had seen the tinker go off on his rounds before I thought it best to think of the horses, — when she seizes me quick by the arm and draws me into the street.

"'Come home! oh, me deary Duvil! come home! come home! all has gone wrong in the camp. The tinker is mad with his drink.'

A Tale of the Roads

"My wife, here, could ride before she could walk; so we wait for no saddles, but, mounting and leading the rest of the horses by their long halters, we make off for the common as fast as we can.

"I have in my hand a heavy chuckny, a whip, with lead in the handle ; and for this I am glad and thank God, as we come in sight of the tents.

"The tinker is sitting crouched on his cart, goading the great dog with the long branch he has torn from a thorn-tree, and setting the furious beast on his wife, who fights it away with her bare, bleeding hands, not daring to turn from it, or run to a shelter, lest it throw her down to the earth. The tinker laughs like a fiend, as he crouches upon the cart. That is the only sound, save the growls of the dog; for Betty utters no cry as she fights the savage brute off.

"Young man, it was many long years ago that this happened ; but even now to think of it makes my heart stop in its beating, and brings the sweat to my

195

brow. It made me quail then; but, praise God, I am no coward, and I had the heavy whip in my hand.

"As he sees us, the tinker lashes the dog with a wild cry, till it springs, blind with pain, at the throat of the Gypsy girl who stands silent. But I spring too; I leap from the gry and I strike down the dog with the heavy whip-handle, and it lies still at her feet, as though it were dead, though it is not, only stunned by the blow.

"Then the tinker comes from his place on the cart to struggle with me for the whip, which I throw from me to where my wife stands, and she catches it up, so keeping him or me from doing murder. Twice I strike him down with my mawleys, twice he rises and comes at me again. But the third time he goes down with his face bleeding, and I know he is satisfied; for he has no strength to rise or to stand before me again. So I turned to Betty, his wife.

"'Will you come with us now, and leave this man forever?' I asked her.

"But she answered me only: —

"'I will stay with my husband.'

"We take up our tent, stowing it under the wagon; we tie the horses so they will lead, then fasten them all to the back of the van; we gather everything that is ours into the vardo, saying never a word until it is done.

"'Will you come with us now?' I asks her again, 'or will you stay with this man till he kills you?'

"'I will stay with my husband,' she answers. 'Go your ways, I have chosen my choice. I fears nothing. Go on your ways, and leave me alone with my husband.'

"Saying this, she goes to him as he lies on the grass, taking his head in her lap, bathing the red stains from his face, speaking to him, low and softly, words which we cannot hear.

"My wife and I would not go until after the sunset. But for all that we said she had only one answer: she would stay with her husband. At last the tinker got up from the ground; and the dog, at the sound of his voice, stood up also, growling at us, snapping at the heels of the grys.

"'Will you come?' I asked her again.

"'I will not go with you,' she answered; 'I will stay with my husband.'

"'Go on,' cried the tinker, catching up stones from the earth. 'Go on. Let the woman alone. She is mine to do with as I will, to beat or to kill at my pleasure. She knows it; she makes no complaint. Go on, if you fear for your lives.'

"'You will not come?' I called once again.

"'I will stay with my husband,' she answered, turning away from my wife's pleading, to smile in the tinker's black face.

"So we drove on perforce, none too soon, as it proved; for a stone struck the van, then another and another, till one broke through the top, to fall brushing my wife's dress and striking her foot. So I was glad enough to whip the horses

198

into a gallop, and get out of the reach of
the tinker's sure aim.

"We never saw her again. News
reached us that she died the next week
in a cave in a glen where they were
camping, somewhere in the next county
to this, — died of a fever some said; but
no one saw her or knows where she is
buried. And I think that a cave is a
dark place, and that much might happen
there which the sheriff knows nothing
about, much that my own people thinks
best to let be as it is. And I think she
met a foul death, most likely clinging
to him, still saying her soft words until
the end came.

"And I think that no man knows
where she lies buried, because she was
never put into the earth. And I think
if I searched in the long metal boxes
that lie under the others on the tinker's
cart I should find something of her;
for once when I met him, long after,
walking beside his great dog and pulling
his cart, under the arched trees in a
Florida hummock, where the grey moss

hung down from the live oaks to brush him, I heard a strange rattle, like the rattling of dry bones together, and I smelled a strange smell like nothing I ever knew of before. And the sound and the smell both came from the long boxes piled on the cart under the others; and I need not say to you what I think was hidden in them."

We drove on in silence awhile, watching the clouds break and the faint afternoon sunlight flood through them to gild the roofs of my town, as it lay at peace on the lap of the hillside.

"Let us make the camp over the bridge by the creek, to the west of the town," said Mr. Lovell.

"It is a good place for a fire, and there is shade for the tents. I remember it well. Let us camp there, though there is but little grass for the grys," good Mrs. Lovell made answer from her seat on the floor of the van, just behind us.

"Did you ever see the tinker again, Mr. Lovell?" I asked.

A Tale of the Roads

"I have seen him twice since: the last time as I told you; but three years ago, in the Tennessee mountains, where he was with his dog and his cart. But we speak not to each other in passing, and our eyes do not meet. Nor do my people often pass him apray the droms; for wherever he goes he leaves his patteran, the long cross drawn in the dust, pointing the way he has taken. Seeing this, my people turn aside into other ways, that they may not come up with him on the road."

"But others may use the same patteran?"

"So they may, pal, if they wish; but none but the tinker ever draw the skull and cross bones where the lines meet, as he does, and, seeing this, my people will not follow, but turn them aside.

"If you ever see him, rye, you will know him by that devil's own dog of his, and by the devil's own look in his eye."

IV

Now, though this story of Mr. Lovell's made no slight impression upon me at the time, I soon forgot all about it; and when, some months later, I stood one day early in October on the bank of the Kokosing, where it flows past the foot of the town, watching the workmen as they laid the great stones in place which were to form the arches of a stout viaduct over the stream, thinking how sad a thing it was to know that the old covered bridge which had so long spanned the clear flowing river was now a thing of the past, never again to bear on its broad beams the motley throng that had crossed it, never again to echo the clatter of hoofs or the rumble and rattle of wheels, never again to shelter under its shingles, out of the dust or the wind or the pelting rain, the old and the young, the sad and the gay, as it had sheltered them all in the good times gone by, — as I say, the story that

A Tale of the Roads

Mr. Lovell had told me had so faded out of my mind, that I stood for some moments looking over the river at a man and a dog drawing a heavy cart after them slowly and wearily down to the stream without realising that there, before me, just over the water, coming toward me, was the tinker, with his great dog and the low cart with the boxes and all.

The yellow light came out of the west, shining under the heavy bank of leaden clouds which hung low over the woods to the east, glaring on the cool grey of the water, breaking into ruddy gold over the ripples. It was sunset. I went slowly down the path at my right, by some willows and across the long, narrow foot-bridge, carelessly built of old rafters and bridge-boards, to be used by pedestrians till the viaduct should be completed; I went slowly across, while slowly down to the foot-bridge toward me came the man and the dog, drawing the cart.

As we drew nearer each other, I could

see that his face was long, sullen, grey, and grey-bearded; that his dog, too, was grey; and that the pieces of canvas thrown over the cart were likewise faded and grey. And as we drew still nearer I knew him, indeed, by the devil's own dog which stalked at his side, and by the devil's own look which lurked in the man's wild eye.

The tinker paused when he reached the bridge, and I saw him set his heavy foot upon the light rafters and shake its slight rail with his heavy hand, trying its strength, as I knew, when he glanced over his shoulder back at the cart.

"It will bear you with the wagon and the dog too," I said, as I paused on the bridge above him, for there were steps leading down at that end. "It will bear double the weight."

"It looks but a weak thing," he answered, and, advancing as far as the harness he wore on his shoulders allowed, he set his heavy foot once again on the bridge, stamping upon it. Years before a road circus had entered the town by

A Tale of the Roads

the old covered bridge, van after van passing over, bearing lions and tigers and leopards in cages hidden by the canvas covers which protected the carvings and gilt from the dust and the rain. All passed over, lion and leopard and tiger in cages, the camels led by their drivers. All went by the bridge till the elephant came, with its slow, swinging stride, last of the caravan. It set its foot on the bridge, stamping twice, as the tinker had done, then turned down and forded the river, blowing the water high in the air from its trunk, and so entered the town with its sides dripping.

I thought of this as the tinker stood testing the planking.

"It will bear you," I said again. "I have seen half-a-dozen wheelbarrows loaded with sand run up a board over these steps and toted across, the men walking one after the other."

"There is no other bridge near?"

"None within half a mile."

"Then I will cross here."

He would have lifted his cart up the

few steps unaided had the task been a possible one, so loath did he seem to hold conversation with me or with those who had come up behind him, waiting to cross; but as his strength was not equal to it, he turned sullenly to ask our assistance.

" Will you lend a hand up the steps," he asked.

Going round to the rear of the cart I took hold with some others. In a moment we had it safe on the bridge. The tinker gave us no thanks for our pains, but moved slowly away, drawing the cart over the creaking timbers. As he did so, I heard a strange rattling sound, while a strange faint odour came back to me as I followed. And I thought of the long tin boxes under the others, and of the words Mr. Lovell had spoken.

He did not pause at the end of the bridge; nor did he ever once turn his head to look back. But as he reached the crest of the gentle incline I moved forward quickly, and going close to his side, asked, as I looked in his face:

A Tale of the Road

"Rakessa tu Rommanes? Do you speak Gypsy?"

If he started, the movement was so slight it escaped me; but I saw a change in his eyes.

"What did you say?" he asked, coming to a standstill, and looking at me. "I did not hear you."

"Rakessa tu Rommanes?" I repeated. "Do you speak Gypsy?"

"I do not speak Gypsy," he answered. "I know nothing about the Gypsies. Why do you ask me?"

"I thought you might have known them, being a tinker. Have you seen any on the roads?"

"I have seen none for more than a month. It is true that I am a tinker, but I keep to myself. How comes it that you speak Gypsy? You are not one of their people?"

"It may be it comes that I speak it, as it comes that you do not understand it, you who are one of their people."

"Tute jins chomany, you know a thing or two," said the tinker, and turned him away with the Rommany words on his lips giving the lie to the words he had spoken.

"Shall tute jal on ke ratti? — shall you go on to-night?" I called after him.

"Mandy must jal to the gav over the hills," he replied, and so indeed went on to the town over the hills, taking the road to the right, which led to the eastward.

In the morning, following this road, I soon came upon the patteran marked in the sand, — the long cross pointing the way he had taken, with the skull and the cross bones rudely drawn in the dust near the lines. And seeing this, I, too, like the Gypsies, turned me aside and did not follow, for the sinister mark seemed as the cry of a leper, warning all men from his path.

V

"I HAVE seen the end of the tinker, pal," Mr. Lovell said, after we had shaken hands at our next meeting, even before I had told him of seeing the tinker myself.

"Sit down, if you please, rye," Black Katherine said, as she came up to us. "Beshalay. While the kettle is boiling he can tell you about it. There'll be a bit of supper spread on the grass when it is done. I doubt much, however, if the end of the tale finds you in good appetite."

So saying, she busied herself with her work, while Mr. Lovell, filling his pipe from the pouch I extended, stretched himself at his ease on the grass to resume and complete the last summer's recital.

"It happened in this here way, rye. There were too many of us camping together near a small town, — some of the Coopers, and Stanleys, with more of the Lovells. The town could not support us. There were few fortunes to tell, few horses to trade, and one of my cousins, being pressed by the bad times, passed off a little counterfeit money.

"It was quick work to break camp,

14   209

to get the wheels turning, and the vans
out of sight before the sheriff could be
upon us. But we do it; and they get
well off into the next county before
harm could befall them.

"Now as I have business to keep me,
and am well known in the town, I stay
behind to settle my own affairs, when
the storm has blown by, as it does in a
few days.

"Having settled my own affairs with
the trader, I mounts the horse I have
kept with me, and am going upon my
way to a certain place in the hilly
country where I know I shall find Mrs.
Lovell and my own people, the others
having scattered, of course, as fast as
they could to elude any pursuit.

"I go but a little way out of town,
however, when I come up with a farming mush who eyes my horse, which is
but a poor thing; and I presently falls
into a conversation with him, before long
selling him the gry for a very good
price, which I pockets, and walks off,
leaving the horse with the farmer, mean-

ing to buy another when I sees one to my fancy. But I found none I fancied, and perforce continued my journey on foot. The next day I come into the heart of a rough, lonely country where the hemlock and pine grow out of the great rocks which rise high over the river, and where the hills are much furrowed by deep clefts and ravines. When I reach this country, I know I have not far to go.

"Here on a wild, narrow road which ran by the river, late in the afternoon, a heavy thunderstorm overtook me, and I was glad to make my way down a narrower path, to stand at the edge of the river under the great rocks, out of the driving rain.

"As I stood there, I saw a cleft in the hillside where no rain seemed to penetrate, and making my way as best I could over the slippery stones, I entered the opening, and found myself in the mouth of a long narrow chasm, the floor uneven but dry, the ceiling lofty, formed of huge boulders that had lodged in the

seam. Curiosity prompting me, I went
up the slight incline, groping my way in
the half darkness, stumbling over loose
fragments of rock, once sprawling at full
length on the soft, dry sand which was
slowly filling the place, on up the incline until I reached what seemed to be
the end of the cavern, some thirty or
forty feet from the entrance. Here,
pal, I paused of necessity; for the walls
grew together, leaving a high, narrow
aperture scarcely a foot wide. Looking through this, I saw that the rift
widened again into a wider and deeper
cavern than that in which I had sheltered myself from the rain. I saw, too,
that the narrow aperture had served on
the side from which I approached as a
barrier to hold back the sand and
broken stones from falling into the
larger cave, so that, as I stood looking
through into the further cavern, I was
fully ten feet above its level, standing
as I did at the head of the incline. As
I made these observations in the dim
light, I heard a rattling of loose

stones, and, pitiful God! think of it,
rye! there stood the tinker, his dog,
and his cart at the other end of the
cave.

"I drew quickly back from the opening, fearing his devil's own eye could see
in the dark, or that his devil's own dog
might sniff me. I was for leaving the
shelter; but when I came to the door
of the cavern, the rain beat down upon
the river, the wind roared in the hem-
locks and pines, the thunder boomed
and rattled and echoed above so fear-
fully that I was glad to turn back into
the place again. Then I bethought me
that, although I could see the tinker
quite clearly, it was not likely that he
could observe me, as my cavern was
narrow and dark, and my point of ob-
servation some ten feet above him. So
I stole back to the crevice, and, stretching myself out in the soft sand which
had collected there, looked down on
the tinker below me.

"'I have,' said the tinker, addressing
himself or his dog, or both, — 'I have

passed by this place a score of times, which is twenty, and never once entered it since I entered it with her and left it alone. Rain and wind, lightning and thunder, never drove me hither before. It is the vast of the beng, the hand of the devil, which has drawn me here now. My dog, my boro juckle, you will well recollect what she said to me then. "There will come a day when you will come here alone, and a night when you shall sit here on the sand of this cave alone; and when that day and that night come, you will gladly give all the world to have me beside you, — me whom you kill."

"'You will recollect this, my juckle, and you will know that I am not here alone, but that she is here with me now.'

"As I looked I saw him stretch forth his heavy hand and shake the cart at his side. As he did so, amid the clatter of iron I heard a dry, rattling sound, and a faint sickly odour stole into the air and clung to my nostrils.

A Tale of the Roads

"'She is here with us now. Her soul is here, wandering in the dark rocks; and her body is here; and the love which was mine is still mine. She is here! She is here!'

"Again his heavy hand shook the cart, again I heard the faint rattle, again the strange odour pervaded the place.

"'She is here,' he cried wildly. 'She is mine, mine forever! Let the rain fall, let the thunder roll, let the blue lightning gleam! What care we; we three are together, — the tinker's dog, and the tinker's wife, and the tinker.'

"Then in a wild voice he sang a wild gillie, while the great dog shrunk away, to cower by the cart with its head hung down and its tail wagging slowly, fearing the tinker, dumb brute as it was, the thunder rumbling and crashing overhead.

"'Oh, the Rommany chie for the tinkering mush,
The tinkering mush for the chie.
The lass who was born 'neath a blackberry bush
Is the lass to delight a bold eye.'

" He sat on the floor of the cave as he sang, gathering great handfuls of the loose sand, which he flung high over his head into the air, letting it shower down upon him as he repeated the words of the song over and over, sometimes changing or adding to them wild words of his own.

" At last, tiring of this, or his mood changing as the night came on, he gathered a heap of pine knots together from the door of the cave, where a tree had fallen and rotted, leaving the resinous bunches to be separated by wind and rain from the sodden log. Piling these near the door of the cave, he lighted them, and sat silently watching the bright flame for a while; then he spoke again to the dog.

" ' Here, juckle,' he called, letting his grey face rest on his hands, which were spread out between his knees, and so crouching forward with his face near to the dog's.

" ' Here, juckle, answer my question; why did you kill her? Was it because

A Tale of the Roads

I lashed you, lashed you and lashed you,
and set you upon her that I might see
her fight with her bare hands; or was it
because the devil lives in you? Why
was it, my juckle?'

" The dog only growled, drawing away
from the face which was thrust, with its
terrible leer, so near to its own.

" 'Answer, my juckle! Was it because I lashed you and lashed you, as I
crouched on the top of the cart, which
stood there where it stands now, near
the corner? Was it for that, or for what
that you killed her with your white
teeth? Tell me, my juckle?'

" But the dog growled again, drawing
still further back.

" 'Was n't she kind to you, juckle? —
soft in her voice and her ways. Was it
because you were tired of her low voice
and caresses, or because you hated or
loved her? Tell me, my juckle? Why
was it you tore at her breast with your
sharp teeth? Why was it I gave no
heed to her pleadings, mocking her
prayers as I crouched, out of your way,

217

on the cart?' But the dog only growled
and drew further away.

" 'Was it because the nightman who
comes with the storm had stolen your
heart out and mine to fill in the place
with the lightning, the sky-snake, whose
sting burns more deadly than the cop-
per-head's bite? Was it the sky-snake
that writhed in your heart, or the sting
and the bite of the lash in my hand?
Answer me, juckle?'

"As he spoke, he reached up to the
dog's face, and, taking it in his hands,
while its red lips curled back over its
long fangs, laid his cheek close to the
dog's jowl, paying no heed to the snarl
and the growl, holding the brute fast in
his arms.

" 'Did we love her or hate her? Have
we missed her at night and at morning,
or have we been glad to be free? Have
we waited by copse-wood and common
for her to come up with us on the drom?
Have we left the patteran always for her,
marked in the dust, that her quick eyes
might see? Where is she to-night,

A Tale of the Roads

juckle? Is her soul fast in these dark rocks, or is it roving abroad with the soul of the wind, with the ghosts and the witches who ride over the land on the storm? She is not here with us, juckle. We are all alone, for her soul was the soul of a witch; these rocks could not hold it or keep it for us. We are alone, juckle, alone.'

"The great dog snaps at his face. The tinker starts back with a cry. The dog snaps again. The tinker catches a brand from the fire, lashing the brute into madness, until it has sprung at his breast, and he staggers and falls, with the red flames leaping and laping about him, into the heart of the fire.

"'Is she here? Is she here? Is her soul in the rocks? and the love that was mine, is it mine now? Did she lie when she said that it was mine, mine forever, — did she lie and deceive me? Where is she? She is mine, and I want her. God, do you hear me! I want her! I will give all the world to look once in her face. I want her! I want her!'

Tales of the Real Gypsy

"Unheeding the flames, which were wrapping him fast, he broke the strong lids from the long boxes, and gathered the bones in his hands, with the dust, pressing them close to his breast, to his face, to his lips, as he fell back into the midst of the fire, and lay there without motion or life, wrapt in the clouds of thick smoke which rose to the high rocky ceiling and hung there above him, while the great dog crouched in the furthermost corner.

"I was glad to steal away into the night, glad to find the storm drifting over, but gladdest of all to see here and there a dim star in the sky."

So ended the story.

MY LADY OF EGYPT

MY LADY OF EGYPT

I

THE town was crowded. It was Saturday, Saturday afternoon, too; the heat was most oppressive. Out in the country beyond the town a wonderful haze lay over the dusty fields, hiding the far-off hills, shadowing the woodlands, clinging to the parched yellow pastures.

In and out among the press of farmers' wagons, traps and surreys ventured; along the pavement, mingling with the town and country people, gliding in and out among them, now seen, and now unseen, flashed the red shawls and the dark eyes of the Gypsies.

"And may you be a grandfather before you are ten years older. Now keep a sober head, and so God bless you."

Upon the steps leading into a barber-shop sat the speaker, a little crowd about her, listening to the fortune she

223

was telling a dull, earnest-looking man of middle age, who eyed her wonderingly, as she thus dismissed him.

"She's a good one," said the boots of the barber-shop to a friend, speaking over the shoulders of the others as he could, having the advantage of the topmost step.

"Send her away, you're blocking the door," cried the barber, from within the gloom of his shop.

"Oh, Lord!" sighed my Lady of Egypt. "Indeed, there's no rest for a body."

She took up her staff from its place on the steps beside her; she gathered the little baskets she carried into one hand with her apron corners, — the apron was thus a receptacle for a few small melons which had perhaps been given her for a fortune, or deftly taken for nothing; this accomplished, up rose My Lady of Egypt.

A glance down the street told her that the van for which she was waiting was not yet in sight. She looked past

the row of buildings dwindling to the
river-side, where the street ended, and
beyond them to the misty open country;
but she shook her head; her eyes were
dim, they could not discern through the
haze the distant hill-top where her people were camped.

A crowd collected about her. It was
kindly enough; it meant her no harm.
It was only curious to see her quaint
face and attire.

But My Lady of Egypt was very old;
perhaps for many years she had not
been in so great a press. She turned
from right to left; she was hemmed in
by the good-natured people who meant
her no harm, but who would not let her
pass. They pressed closer, laughing,
as she entreated them for room.

"I am more than a hundred years
old, gentlemen; I know you would do
me no ill; but I am best at my camp-
fire. Let me pass, kindly gentlemen,
let me pass."

Her cheeks — a moment before they
had been red as the bright withered

apples that cling longest to the bare
branch — had grown pale; under her hat
of faded yellow straw her black eyes wandered, frightened, seeking some means
of escape from the crowd, which ever
grew larger. Her hands trembled as
she drew her red shawl close over her
shoulders.

A boy plucked at the shawl; the foremost men laughed. She raised her hand
to make a little space between them,
that she might pass; the corners of her
apron slipped, the melons fell to the
pavement, in an instant they were tram-
pled to pulp. In her fright, she loosened her grasp of the baskets; they too
were broken by the ready hands of the
urchins; one was tossed to the barber's
boy, who waved it above his head, as
he stood on the topmost step. However, it did not escape the fate of its fel-
lows, as it was snatched from his fingers
and sent dancing over the heads of the
laughing crowd, till it fell into the gutter, where it was broken by the heavy
foot of the butcher, who came running

from his shop next door to take part in
the sport.

Quite wild with excitement and fear,
My Lady of Egypt broke through the
crowd, forcing her way with feverish
strength to the free pavement. Then,
as all turned with laughter and cries,
she tried to elude them by flight. But
her steps were slow, and the crowd was
soon up with her, running before her,
beside her, behind her, plucking at her
dress, catching at her arms, urging her
forward by a thousand jesting words
which she did not understand. She
breathed hard; her lips were parted; she
tried to speak to her persecutors, but
her tongue was dry, and no sound came.
She ran on and on; as the panic grew
in her heart, it spread to the crowd's.
The laughter and light words were
hushed; the men ran on silently, then
sullenly; then fierce words were spoken.
Then a hand was raised, too late, another
had tripped her, and My Lady of Egypt
fell fainting by the heavy rail of the
viaduct.

Then a strong arm put the throng aside, making room and way for a herculean Gypsy. Without a word, he raised my Lady of Egypt lightly in his arms and placed her on the straw that covered the floor of the van. Then he turned:

" You first," he cried, and levelled the butcher with one blow; another and another went down before him; then, as the crowd broke and scattered, he caught his heavy whip in his strong hand, and drove them all like cattle back from the viaduct into the town.

When all were beyond the reach of his whip, he shook his clenched hand at them in warning, then turned and went slowly back to the van that was waiting for him.

In a moment he had taken his place by the driver, and the van was gone, bearing My Lady of Egypt to the camp on the distant hill.

My Lady of Egypt

II

HEARING of these things, and of others, of which anon, in the evening I betook myself to the wooded hill-top where, across the way from the little church, I knew the tents of the Gypsies were pitched.

"Sar'san," I said, as I paused at the edge of the circle of light.

The figures about the fire had turned toward me. It was time to speak.

"Rommany chel?" a voice asked.

"Kekker, pal, mandy's a Gorgio!" I answered as I went forward and stood by the fire. "No, brother, I am not a Gypsy." There was an ominous silence.

"Ha! If I ever dicked an ugly Gorgio, you are one. Where did you pick up that slang?"

The hero of the afternoon was still in no pleasant humour. I half repented the trouble I had taken to walk out from the town. I had some vague doubt of the result of my mission; but I assumed

as bold a front as I could with the dogs
sniffing my heels; and when he asked me
again where I had learned the few Gypsy
words I had spoken, I answered with a
confidence more of tongue than of heart:

"Where you did, pal, adra the pauno
tan of an Egyptian. I always keep a few
words sar amande, with me. It's a pleasant evening." Saying this, I sat down
uninvited on a blanket that lay near the
fire, wondering how long hostilities
would continue.

"I guess you're one of those Gorgios that learned to rakker out of a
book." In his hand the hero reflectively
swung the great whip he had used so
effectively on the viaduct in the afternoon. "Well, if you are, I'll give you
the length of this whip for a start, and
then I'll set the dogs on you. You'd
better be going." With this the whip
ceased its swinging, and the Gypsy
moved a step nearer, whistling to his
dogs.

It was no time to be nervous.

"Well, Rommany or Gorgio, which

ever I am, I will just sit here by the yog
until you learn a few civil speeches with
which to beg my pardon, and then, in
due time, I 'll be going."

"So you 've come to the end of your
book-learned Rommany, young man?"

"Not quite," I said, losing my patience a little, but with discretion.
"I 've enough left to sal at tute for a
dinello Roman, to laugh at you for a
fool of a Gypsy. Beshalay! sit down.
I 'll not be going for half the night. Do
the Gorgios come to your camp in the
sarla when there is no chone, no moon,
to light the wesh ? You are dinello!
How many juvas are there in the tan
adoi? Call the chavies in; and where
are the horses? I have come to your
yog, and called you brother; I have
come to give you timely warning; shall
I stay, or shall I jal?" And as I spoke
I arose.

"Stay if you be a friend. What 's
your warning?"

"The Gorgios will be welling out
from the gav in the hour. Get the

horses into the vans. There's to be trouble to-night to pay for the work of your whip on the bridge."

"Ha!" cried the huge Gypsy, starting up fiercely. "The devils would pay us a visit in the dark of the moon. Well, let them come!" He paused suddenly, then, coming to me and laying his heavy hands upon my shoulders, he turned my face full to the firelight.

"You are playing no unmannerly jest, young man?" he asked. "This is tacho, this is truth?"

"It is truth."

"I believe you, pal. There is a look in your eyes that I've seen in the eyes of many Egyptians, though your cheek is white like a Gorgio's. I will not set the juckles on you to-night, and when this business is done you can teach me a civil speech, to ask a gentleman's pardon in, though if you're Rommany chel, you're no gentleman, unless a card-sharper is one, for that's what I take you to be. Give me your hand, brother; no harm's done."

My Lady of Egypt

With a mighty clasp he enfolded my hand in his.

"It's cards or night work of the house-breaking order, by the feel of your fingers. You've not touched a curry-comb since you took to a better business."

III

THE vans stood at considerable distances one from the other; the tents that had been pitched for the night were also separated, placed as they were at intervals through the wooded strip of flat hill-top; even the horses were tied at a distance. It would be impossible to defend the camp as it was.

Even Jack Lovell, the herculean grandson of Mrs. Small, My Lady of Egypt, saw this, and was for placing his grandmother in her great van, and forming a barricade about it with the other wagons. But such a course would have left the score or more of horses unprotected; and as we supposed there would be more danger to apprehend from their being driven off and scattered by the attacking party than from any other source, his judgment was overruled, and it was decided to break camp and move on, if possible, before the night visitants should reach the hill-top.

To this, young Lovell was finally won by the fear that Mrs. Small, who now lay in her tent with a fever brought on by the panic and fright of the afternoon, would be further excited, and her health further endangered, by the noise and confusion of the attack. The night was very dark, the silence heavy and oppressive in the sleeping woods. Noiselessly the Gypsy women moved to and fro in the gloom; the tents were torn down, folded, and packed away; the kettles were hung beneath the wagons; Mrs. Small was carefully lifted into her van, where she rested at ease on the mattress; then the men led up the horses.

There were two horses to draw each van; the others were fastened that they might lead, and then given in charge to one of the young men, who was, at the signal, the call of a whippoorwill, to ride ahead with them, keeping at a safe distance, no matter what should befall the vans. The wisdom of this arrangement was apparent. The enemy could easily cut loose the horses were they fastened behind the wagons.

It was quick work. The fire had been smothered with wet straw and sods, so that its light shone upon none of the wagons, or the figures that moved swiftly among them. One could see nothing. The only sound was the jangle of harness, the champ of bits, and the thud, thud of hoofs, as the horses drew at their bridles or pawed the ground restlessly; only these sounds, with the night sounds and the low-spoken words of the Gypsies.

I thought we should be safe off before the mob came. All was silent down the road; so silent and hushed that a doubt came into my mind of the warning that had been given me, and it seemed to me that I had played a foolish part in bearing the idle talk out from the town in the night to break up the camp, when no danger might threaten. As I stood by the great Lovell's side, I told him something of my thoughts; and as I spoke the silence in the woods seemed to grow into a greater stillness, the peace of the night seemed to deepen.

"It is best that we should be going," he answered. "It may be a false alarm you've given us, but we bear you no ill will for that; you meant well enough."

I caught his arm as he spoke. A dog that had strayed away into the woods to dig up a bone it had buried in the plenty of the morning, growled fiercely. Then we heard a twig break, and the soft crackle of many feet on the fallen leaves.

"There they are now," Lovell whispered to me with an oath, "the sneaking Gorgios! they have come up through the woods. Are you hitched, Jemmy?" he asked of the man on the other side of the horses.

"Yes," came the answer.

236

My Lady of Egypt

"Are Bill's horses in?" He moved a few steps back to the next wagon. "All right, Bill?"

"Yes, all right."

"Move up behind the puro dye's van as close as you can get." Then we passed on to the other wagons. Both were ready to move. By the muffled voices and by the crackling boughs we knew that the enemy was within a hundred yards, coming stealthily on. Jack Lovell swung himself up on the seat beside Jemmy.

"Come on," he said to me; "we may need you." As he spoke, he reached down and, taking my hand, swung me up to the broad seat of the van. His wife was in the back of the wagon with My Lady of Egypt, who now lay very quiet, the fever having abated a little. She was conscious.

"Let us be moving quickly, my son," she said in her faint voice. "God bless me, I am too old to have heart for such doings."

"Avali, dya, yes, mother." As he

ceased speaking here came from his lips the clear note of a whippoorwill; ere its echo had died away in the colonnades of the forest the wheels of Bill Lovell's van were in motion, followed by the two other vans.

" Don't start the horses till Bill is close behind us," Lovell said to his brother. " We must keep together. It is careful driving in the woods. You 've got the gun? "

" Don't use it," I said.

" Use it if you need, Jemmy. They 've had all the sport with the puro dye they are going to have. There they come! "

As he spoke, a great yell went up from the woods. The enemy had heard the turning of the wheels; they knew their prey was escaping. With a wild rush they came forward upon the vans.

" Start the horses, lash them! " Lovell cried, bringing his whip down upon those his brother was driving.

Too late! The bridles were seized by the foremost of those who had rushed from their cover.

My Lady of Egypt

In the instant the three vans came up and passed.

"Go on!" Lovell shouted; "go on! we will follow." As he spoke, he stepped out on the tongue of the wagon, bringing his whip down again and again on the heads and shoulders of those who held the horses and on the horses themselves.

Oaths and cries answered the sting and cut of the lash in the air. The horses, maddened, rose on their haunches, then dashed forward, drawing the great van, heavy and reluctant with its weight of carving, gilt, and mirrors, over fallen logs and roots and stumps, that shook us almost from our seats as the wheels passed above them; and so, with a mighty straining of girths and buckles, and tried sinews too, with a mighty ring of Gypsy words urging the horses out upon the highway, free of the treacherous woods, and sweeping down the road, rolled the great van.

"Shall we wait?" called Bill from before us.

"Go on! We are clear of the cowards," Jack shouted to him, and the wagons went on.

We could hear the baffled mob running behind us, but we had no fear. The horses were galloping. The great van once rolling over the even drom no longer held them back. Very soon we should distance our pursuers.

We passed the church, swept on over the stretch of level. The danger was almost over. The pursuers were two hundred yards down the road, just breaking out of the woods as hounds break cover following a fox that strikes through the open.

"Damn them! They get off too easy!" I heard Lovell mutter. And then snap! And the van veered to one side. The off horse was thrown violently against the other; a tug had broken.

Lovell was down in the road in an instant, a piece of chain in his hands, with a hook at one end to mend the harness. He fastened the hooked end to the cross bar; the long end of the

240

tug he tied into a knot with his powerful hands, and he was attempting to bind
the chain to it with some leather thongs
Jemmy had thrown him, when the shout-
ing mob was about us again.

He was unarmed; he had left his
heavy whip in my hands. Jemmy had
the horses to think of. There was but
one thing to do; our only chance lay
in Lovell's strong arm.

I leaped to the ground, took the
thongs from him, gave him the heavy
whip.

" Keep them back till I tie it," I said;
and then I set to work with the tug and
the chain, lashing the twisted chain fast
beyond the knot, past which I knew that
the cords would not let it slip. As I
worked, I knew the mob surged all
about me, jostled me, almost lifted me
from the earth with the press of their
bodies; but I kept on with the thongs,
winding them round and round the
chain and the tug, leaving the rest to
the Lovells.

Again and again Lovell beat them

16   241

away, not always, as I could tell by the
sound of its falling, with the lash, but
with the heavy end of the whip. It was
sickening to hear it, and the cries and
curses that followed its falling. But
there was nothing for it. He was keeping twenty men back.

I made the last twist; I tried it, I
knew it would hold. I knotted the
cords. As I did so, I felt a man fall
across my feet, half under the horses;
I almost trod upon him as he lay. I
knotted the cords again, then stooped
to draw the man from the hoofs of the
horses and from the path of the wheels,
which otherwise would have gone over
him as the van started. I drew him a
little way, as I did so calling to Jemmy
that the tug was mended and to Jack
to get into the van, when I heard a stone
strike the wheel just beside me, and
then something struck me. All that I
knew was that the wheel I caught at in
my falling was beginning slowly to turn,
then I felt myself lifted, then something
moving beneath me.

My Lady of Egypt

IV

THE horses were walking when I recovered consciousness. I moved a little, trying to rise from the floor of the van. Slowly I realised that my head rested, not entirely at ease, on Jack Lovell's knee ; that one of his hands held a cold bandage upon my head, while the other supported and steadied me so that I felt the movement of the van very little.

" Are we all here ? " I asked, finding that I had a rather faint voice. " No harm done ? "

" Ha ! God bless me ! " echoed a fainter voice from the depths of the van. " Is that the naflo mush, the sick young man ? "

" Ava, dya, yes, mother," I answered for myself. " Only of what I am sick I do not know, nor that I am sick at all, for that matter."

" How is your head, pal ? Mandy 's been holding this wet rag where the

stone struck you ever since we passed
the last house, where I got the pani, the
water. Mandy guesses he mored the
Gorgio that wusted it at tute. Mandy
delled leste a tatto yeck apray the nock,
with the chuckny, and left him stretched
like a bit of shillo mass adra the drom.
I guess I killed the Gorgio that threw
it at you. I gave him a hot one on the
nose with the whip, and left him stretched
like a bit of cold meat upon the road."

"But how did you get me into the
van, pal?" I asked.

"Lifted you with my bango wast, my
left hand, while I beat them off with my
free arm. It was as much as mandy
could do. It would have been more, if
the ones I hit with the heavy end of the
whip had not stayed quietly where I
dropped them."

On and on we went in the blackness.
When no one spoke, I would seem to
lose myself in the van ; my head was
light still, and ached from the blow.
Unless I closed my eyes tightly, or some
hand touched me, or some voice spoke

244

to me, I would seem to drift away out of the van and be left alone in the midst of the night upon the road, that moved and rocked under me. It was a strange sensation, with something a little uncanny and fearful in it, when I remembered the scenes through which we had passed. Indeed, had I known, I should have been very glad when I sank into a heavy sleep, with my head, I suppose, still pillowed on Jack Lovell's knee.

The first light of dawn found us twenty miles or more to the east of our starting-point, crossing a long wooden bridge over a broad river whose waters flowed swiftly and eagerly on to the eastward, murmuring as they went as though they were hurrying away from the night to welcome the morning.

A little farther on we passed through a sleepy village, from whose chimneys the first smoke was streaming up into the paling sky, from which all the stars were not yet vanished.

A few dogs came to their gates and barked at us as we went down the single

street of the hamlet, a few doors stood
ajar, a few housewives were drawing
water up from the depths of the cool,
old-fashioned wells, a few roosters crowed
from their coops behind the houses; it
was all very tranquil, all very idyllic.

I wondered, as I looked out from the
Gypsy van, what the world would be like
if it were always illumined with the pale
grey light of the early morning; how
people would think and live in a misty
land where the smoke from the chimneys
rose so white against the faint flush of
the sky; would we spoil this time, if we
could, as we have spoiled the greater
glow and glory of the day with the
shadows and the tumults and the narrow
hardness of our lives?

Beyond the village we came to a
stretch of no-man's land by the canal,
a well-known camping-ground of the
Romans. Here the caravan paused, and
here, as the day grew, arose the tents of
the Egyptians, and crackled their fires
under the kettles; here grazed their
horses, and here, on the sunny stretch

of the common, gambolled and frolicked their children.

Here I stayed with my new friends, the days passing so idly and pleasantly that there was no temptation to be gone back to the town on the hill about which the Kokosing half circles.

Here all day long I could wander by the river, the broad Walhonding; or along the tow-path by the canal, or on the high hills that rose back of the village, where I frequently wended to get the great stretch of old King White-Eye's Plain all in my view, as I could from their crests. Below me the little hamlet nestled; faintly wreathed the smoke into the blue from its chimneys and hearths; faintly floated to me the sounds of its busy mill-wheels and forge; more faintly, more sweetly, the shouts and the laughter of its children.

Then, as evening stole from the eastern horizon the last glow of sunlight and set the pale stars twinkling, slowly I would betake me along the path down the hillside, loitering, perhaps, through

the village, wishing to enter at each half-
open gate that seemed to invite me;
passing here and there a house that had
drawn close to the street in a friendly
way, leaving the door ajar that I might
catch a glimpse of the family at supper,
— a pleasant glimpse always, — and so
on, on, and on as slowly as might be,
and still on by the narrowing foot-path
to the strip of Kekkeny-mushes-tem —
the no-man's land where the red fires of
the Egyptians threw their sparks high
into the dusky air before tents such as
Abraham might have dwelt beneath
long, long ago.

Then would I sit down by the side of
My Lady of Egypt to the kosko habben,
the good feast, that dark Orlenda, Jack
Lovell's wife, had prepared, spreading it
all on a white cloth at the tent door; and
as I held my great mug of excellent tea
in one hand and my thick piece of rye
bread in the other, I would converse of
many things with the puri Rammani
Rani, the old Gypsy lady.

Now My Lady of Egypt was quite

recovered from the fright and the fever, and there were few better companions than she; many strange notions had she in her mind, and many a strange question she propounded.

"Ha! God bless me!" she began one evening as we sat by the camp-fire,— My Lady of Egypt blessed everything and every one, from a stew in the kettle to her sumptuous van, from a Gypsy to a Gorgio, — "God bless me, my son, the Gorgios look at the tents as if they were strange things. Did not their forefathers once likewise live in tents? Does it not say so in the God's book that tells all about it? Surely they, too, lived in tents?"

V

"So, rye, you wishes to know why my people sometimes call me My Lady of Egypt? It is my title, rye, and it was given to me by a king's son who afterwards was king of England himself, so it cannot be gainsaid. Ha! you opens

your eyes when I speak of the kralis;
yet why should you, rye, for you know
well that I comes of the royal Stanleys,
whose blood is more ancient than any
kralis in the Puro tem, than any king's
in the old country. Ah, God bless you,
my dear, it's a long way back to remember; but since you asks me so
politely, mandy will pen you the true
history of it.

"I was a girl then in England, a
rinkini chie, so the chals penned, and I
wore much fine raiment, as I still do, my
dear, when I visits about among my own
people. We were camped on the heath
near the Nashi Mesero Gav; on Newmarket Heath, my dear, at the time of
the races.

"I was then in the fifteenth year of my
age, — ah, indeed, it is a long way back,
rye, for I am now more than a hundred.
I don't reckon the years now; I just let
them come and go, as they will fast
enough without counting.

"The day was bright, a fine day for the
races, and the gentry were up with their

gay coaches from their fine seats in the country, and the swells were down from the Boro-Gav, London, ha! and the Egyptians were there, too, and we all of us loved the fine sport, and had our interests to serve; the ranis, the ladies, were there to be seen by their lovers, and the ryes had their wagers to make, and the Gypsies their fortunes to tell.

"So in the morning my dye penned to mandy, penned lati, ' Make yourself well to look on, my dear, for you must jal with me to the race-track to dukker the ranis.'

"I remember well the dress that I wore, — a skirt of fine green cloth with a gold tinsel border, and a jacket of red velvet, trimmed, too, with the bright tinsel and fastened by gold guinea pieces. At my throat I wore many strands of coral beads, and in my black hair were braided strings of pearl beads and amber. Indeed I was misto to dick, good to see, from the crown of my head to my feet in their red shoes with the high heels that a Gorgio rani had given me for a fortune, because they were too tight for her wearing.

" My mother, Caroline Cooper, was dressed in the true Gypsy fashion, wearing a great beaver bonnet and a long cloak of scarlet. Round her throat she wore the finest corals in England, and on her hands were many rings, three of tacho bar, of diamonds, finer than many an earl's lady has; and these I secretly envied my mother, for I had no rings, disdaining to wear any less costly than hers.

" So we crossed over Newmarket Heath and came to the race-course, where we met many of our own people, all of them trying to coax the shillings and pence out of the Gorgios' putsies, the Gentiles' pockets. One of my cousins played a trick with a pea and thimble; another let the Gorgios shy sticks at a cocoanut, for which, when one knocked it over, he was well paid by those who had missed it. My uncle was trading horses, while all the little boys begged, and the women told fortunes, and, when they could, passed off a little bad money, or filched a purse out of a rani's putsie.

"Presently we got among the coaches, and my dye dukkered and dukkered, bidding me do likewise; but from shame and fear, being so young, I hung back.

"At last I lost sight of my mother, and in searching for her I came to some carriages that stood separated by a little space from the others. There were many servants in bright liveries about these carriages, who seemed busy unpacking the hampers, while the ryes and the ranis held their field-glasses up to their eyes, watching the horses as they went round the far side of the track.

"As I came near to the carriages, the servants looked up and motioned to me not to approach; but I paid no heed to them, still advancing, thinking I saw my mother beyond them.

"Then all the ryes stood up in the carriages, and the ranis waved their handkerchiefs, and even the lackeys left

off motioning me away to watch the
horses come in so gallantly.

"' I have lost ten pound to you, Mrs.
Fitz-Herbert,' I heard a stout handsome
gentleman say to a beautiful lady who
sat beside him in the finest coach of
them all. 'Shall I pay it in gloves or
in bon-bons ? '

"' In whichever your Highness
pleases.'

"' Then let it be bon-bons,' he bent
close to her as he whispered, ' sweets
to the sweetest; ' but I heard, for I was
just by the steps of the carriage.

"The blood that came to the lady's
pale face was pretty to see. When I
knew I was standing so close to the
Prince of Wales and the poor hapless
lady who was his wife, a fright came
upon me so that I could not move on,
and I would have sunk down to the
earth, had I not clung to the door of
the coach.

"Then, as the servants would have
driven me away, calling me a troublesome beggar under their breaths, and

not gently as they seized my arms to
lead me from the carriage, — then, when
I was all covered with confusion and
shame, my lady held out her hand to
stop the lackeys, and said in a very
sweet voice, —

"'She is doing no harm. What is
it, my dear? Don't be afraid. Have
you come to tell me a fortune?'

"So the lackeys bowed very low,
drawing back, and I went up to the
steps of the carriage again, more at
ease at her words.

"'You are a Gypsy?' the Prince
of Wales asked. 'And what may your
name be?'

"'My name is Theresa, and I come
of the royal Stanleys, if you please, sir,'
and I makes my very best courtesy,
'and my people are all true Egyptians,' and I courtesied again.

"'And, God bless me! who are the
royal Stanleys, my dear? I did not
know there were two royal families in
England,' says his Royal Highness, smiling a little.

"'Oh sir,' I answers, 'the Stanleys are royal wherever they go. They were once kings of Egypt, and my father is now called Pharaoh by our people.'

"'Why, God bless me, do you hear this, Mrs. Fitz-Herbert?' and then turning to me, 'I must call you My Lady of Egypt. Your title is far more ancient than mine. I see there are realms within realms, and more kings than one in these British Isles.'

"'Indeed, sir, there are the royal Faws of Scotland, who were my mother's people. But all the Rommany Krals, all the Gypsy Kings that I know, acknowledge his Majesty King George.'

"'God bless him,' the Prince said, raising his hat. 'So then, my child, they acknowledge my father. But it's little tribute they pay him, and it's much false money they help to circulate throughout his realm.' He paused, and then, laughing, 'Ha, God bless me, I forgot. All kings have the right to coin. Your father should put his own face on the sovereigns he makes.'

My Lady of Egypt

"There I caught him.

"'Oh, no, sir, what would be the use of that when he only coins for his Majesty's subjects?'

"When the Prince began to laugh, which he did quite soon after I had spoken, but not so soon as the pale lady he called Mrs. Fitz-Herbert, then all the ladies and gentlemen of the party who had gathered about laughed also, and seemed to enjoy it very much.

"'How does it chance, My Lady of Egypt,' he asked when they had done with their laughter, — 'how does it chance that your royal father and mother permit you to go about telling fortunes at fairs and race-courses?'

"'We are but a poor broken people, your Highness, and it is many thousand miles to my father's country in Egypt, so far that they cannot send him their tribute. We are pilgrims doing penance for our sins. We bring nothing with us, and we only ask from each what he can give, and in return we reads him his future. Surely, your Highness, it is worth something to have the future read to you.'

"'Can you tell a good fortune?' he asked.

"'I can read the past and the future, your Highness,' I answered.

"He looked at the lady beside him.

"'Shall you be the first?' he asked her, smiling.

"But she did not smile in return.

"'No, no, I cannot bring myself to it. It is foolish; but I dare not, I fear the future. Let the child read your hand. There will be enough of my fortune in it.'

"To cover her embarrassment, the Prince of Wales did as she bade him, and with the tips of my fingers I touched the royal hand. It was a rather plump hand and shapely and soft, and the fingers were long and white; but it was a hand that soon flushed, and the palm was quite mottled, the blood flowing into it as he reached down to me. All drew back out of hearing save Mrs. Fitz-Herbert, who kept her place at his side.

My Lady of Egypt

" ' Shall I ever be king?' he asked me, a slight shade coming over his handsome face.

" ' You will be King of England,' I answered, looking up in his face. At my words I saw that it lighted, and he turned a high look on the lady beside him; but he only said, —

" ' You hear, Mrs. Fitz-Herbert!'

" And she only smiled.

" He listened very closely to all that I said, as the lady listened who sat at his side; and I know that what I said pleased them both, as I took pains that it should.

" ' Tell us,' the lady asked softly at last, ' is his heart constant, child?'

" He turned a most loving look upon her as she asked this, and I am sure that he took her hand in his free hand and pressed it.

" ' Yes, my lady, he is very constant. He will love but two women, though others may think he has loved them. He will love but his mother and one other.' I paused.

" 'Go on, child,' he said, and I think his voice faltered, and I know his hand trembled a little, as I well could know, for I held it lightly in mine. 'Go on, my dear, and the other?'

" 'You will be crossed in your love, but not completely, and you will be forced to put away the one you love and to marry one whom you do not love. But you will be true in your heart to the woman who loves you, and no woman shall ever be crowned as your queen because she cannot sit on your throne.'

" 'Damme! but you are right,' cried the prince; and you know, my dear, the princess he married was never crowned, but was turned back from the doors of Westminster Abbey on the day of his coronation. I was in London when it all chanced.

" 'But he will love me?' the lady asked.

" 'Always and truly,' I answered.

" 'I am content, then,' she said; and as she spoke she drew from her finger a glittering ring, finer to dick than any my mother wore on her hands, and gave it to me.

" ' Let me pay for this fortune,' she said gently, ' by the gift of this jewel. Keep it always, my dear, and when you look at it glistening on your hand, think that it is the tear of a woman who was not altogether unhappy, because she was well loved.'

" As she spoke, she slipped the ring on my finger. See, this is the same ring now, rye."

And Mrs. Small held up her withered hand that I might see again a diamond of great value quaintly set in silver and gold, the white splendour of which I had often admired. Then she continued, —

" As she said this, tears came quickly into the Prince of Wales' eyes, and I was glad to turn away from the coach, lest I should seem over-bold. But he called me back to thank me, and on his face and the face of the lady beside him there was no trace of what I had seen a moment before; both were smiling.

"Seeing this, all the ryes and the ranis returned to their places, and the prince told them that I had penned a merry dukkerin, a tacho fortune.

"There was much confusion, all wishing to be dukkered by me since I had dukkered his Highness. But I thought only to go to my mother, whom I now saw in the distance beckoning to me. Seeing that this was my wish, the lady whispered to the prince, who stepped down from his carriage with a high look on his face, and took my hand, touching only the tips of my fingers.

"'Make way, if you please, for My Lady of Egypt,' he said, as he led me through the crowd to the open beyond. 'I hope we shall meet again, my dear; but should we not, I will still remember the fortune that was told me by My Lady of Egypt on Newmarket Heath. So God bless you!'

"Then he lifted his hat, I courtesied

262

low, the lady in the coach kissed her hand to me, and that was all."

There was a long pause.

" Those were rare times, rye, and for deportment none could equal the prince, and truly he loved the poor lady.

" Yes, rye, I saw him once again. It was in Lundra — in London. He was an older man then, and a king. I was making my way through the crowded street, wondering what brought all the Gorgios together, when I heard a band playing, and some mounted soldiers rode by to clear the way for King George.

" Ha! there was a great shout when we saw him, a great cheer went up, running all down the crowded street as far as the people could see the men on the box.

" I stood in the front of the line. His carriage passed slowly. He bowed and smiled to the people. Then our eyes met. He saw me. He remembered. He knew me! The hand I had held in my own when I penned his dukkerin on

263

Newmarket Heath now lifted his hat
from his brow, as he bowed low to me
from the carriage.

"'My Lady of Egypt!' he said.

"I courtesied deep. He smiled and
threw me a kiss from the tips of his
fingers, for I was still very comely,
and then he was gone. I never saw the
good King again. But I know that he
did not forget me by a service he did
one of my people.

"My cousin Ben Stanley was tried
and sentenced to be nashed, hanged, for
morin a Gorgio. Then the lawyers
heard of the guldo I've penned you.
In a few days it was known that King
George had put his name to a pardon,
and Ben was free. When they let him
come out of the prison, he came straight
to my father's tent, saying that it was
my doing. For the King had told the
lawyer that he pardoned Ben because
he could not think of hanging the cousin
of My Lady of Egypt."

APPENDIX

APPENDIX

FACTS ABOUT THE GYPSIES

THE supposition is that this strange race belonged to the lowest orders of India, from which country they were gradually driven by their own wandering spirit and by conquest and oppression. Rovers and outcasts they must have been at the time of their exodus, and rovers and outcasts they have remained to the present day.

But that the Gypsy had no other history than the history of the slave, the renegade, and the vagrant, in the land of his nativity, I do not believe. His faithfulness to his race-instinct bespeaks a nobler and more ancient origin than is allowed by the theory that he is the offspring of a mixed community recruited from the various ranks of Indian society. A few hundred years would not suffice to weld together such a heterogeneous mass into a people whose traditions and spirit should survive two thousand years undimmed and promise to live on for as many more. Only the remnant of a vastly ancient race would be able to scatter over the world, to separate into small groups, to live in every land and clime, to experience the sway of every form of government of which history has account or which exists to-day, to know the influence of every form of religion, and yet to be at the close of the nineteenth century what they were in the days of their expulsion from India, what they were in the Middle Ages, in nowise changed or changing, in all lands tellers of fortunes, traders of horses, dealers in mystery. Though separated for hundreds of years and by leagues of space, they all speak the same language and live the same life, alike faithful by the sands of Sahara and by the shores of the Arctic Sea, by the flow of the Ganges and by our own Mississippi.

The spirit of pride and independence so strongly characteristic of the Gypsies is scarcely the heritage of a race whose origin was mean and slavish. A fancy of mine is

Facts about the Gypsies

that the ancestors of our friends of the road
were once a sovereign race in India, a race
— like the Arabs — of warrior kings; that
conquest and subjection followed their su-
premacy, and that they slowly sank into the
degraded condition that prevailed before
the beginning of their exodus, still cherish-
ing their pride and their free spirit while
cringing to their conquerors, the pitiful remnant of a prehistoric race.

That they passed through Persia and
Greece their language testifies, as it also
testifies to their vast antiquity, being closely
allied to the Sanskrit. That, immediately
prior to their entrance into Europe, a large
body of them spent some time in Egypt, is
matter of history. From this fact comes
their name, — Egyptians, 'Gyptians, Gypsies.

They first appeared in Europe before the
twelfth century, and in the fourteenth century their numbers were largely augmented.
The first notice of them in European litera-
ture occurs in the writings of an Austrian
monk about 1122, who describes them as
" Ishmaelites," and says of them, much as
we might say to-day, that they " go about
peddling through the wide world, having

neither house nor home, cheating the people
with their tricks, and deceiving mankind, but
not openly."

In 1417 a band of three hundred wanderers, black as Tartars and calling themselves Secani, appeared at the gates of the
German cities. At their head rode a duke
and a count, splendidly dressed, and leading,
like nobles, dogs of the chase ; next came a
motley crew afoot, the women and children
bringing up the rear in wagons. They bore
letters of safe conduct from the Emperor
Sigismund. In 1418 they appeared to the
number of one thousand at the gates of
Zurich, led by " Duke Michael of Little
Egypt." In 1422, according to the chronicle
of Stumpf, the old Swiss historian, fourteen
thousand of these " rogues and vagabonds "
presented themselves at Basel. On the 17th
of August, 1427, a band of them coming
from Bohemia approached the gates of Paris,
which they were not permitted to enter, the
authorities appointing La Chapelle Saint
Denis as their place of lodgment. These
also were headed by a duke and count, and
the company comprised ten other mounted
pilgrims, late renegades of Lower Egypt,

whose women practised palmistry and cleared everybody's pockets.

So the Gypsies swept over Europe, penetrating to the remotest parts, telling strange stories of themselves; and day by day the hands that had been extended to welcome them were turned against them and their practices. Their favourite account of themselves was that they came originally from Egypt, and that their wanderings were a self-imposed penance for a temporary abandonment of the Christian faith. Another account which they frequently gave was that the pope Martin V. had imposed upon them seven years of wandering, during which they were not to sleep in beds, as a means of expiating their sins.

But persecution soon began against them, and once afoot it followed them swiftly and ruthlessly down the centuries. They were banished, outlawed, burned, hanged, tortured, driven from place to place; those who sheltered or protected them too often shared their fate. Francis I. ordered them to quit France on pain of being sent to the galleys without trial whenever taken. In 1560 they were condemned to perpetual

banishment. Decrees were issued against
them in England by Henry VIII. and by
Elizabeth. Sir Matthew Hale mentions
thirteen Gypsies being caught and hanged
at the Suffolk assizes for having neglected to
obey the order to "void the realm" within
thirty days. Edict after edict was issued
against them in all countries, and even as
late as 1748, Frederick the Great renewed
the law that every Gypsy beyond the age of
eighteen found in his states should be hanged
forthwith.

In Scotland they were more kindly re-
ceived. In 1530 Gypsies "dansit before
the King in Holyrudehous." Johnnie Faw
was recognised by James V. as "Lord and
earle of Little Egypt," and authority was
granted him to hang and punish all Egyptians within the realm, sheriffs and other
officers being charged to assist him in the
government of his turbulent subjects. It is
this same Johnnie Faw who furnished Mr.
S. R. Crockett with the hero of his delightful
novel, "The Raiders." But in 1541 an act
was passed that the "Egyptians pass forth
of the realm," under pain of death. In
1624 Helen Faw, a descendant of the

Facts about the Gypsies

"Lord and earle of Little Egypt," together with fifteen other women of her family, was condemned to be drowned. However, in 1657, "King John Buclle" was buried beside Athilstan in Malmesbury Abbey, which indicates that Gypsies were held in some respect.

More recently measures less brutal have been adopted by the governments of Europe toward these nomads. Maria Theresa interested herself in the education of their children and in the gradual settlement of the race as tillers of the soil. These efforts were persevered in by Joseph II., and Hungary and Transylvania number thousands of them among their settled populations. No other countries have succeeded in winning them from their wandering habits, and it cannot be said, judging from Mrs. Pennell's account of their condition in Hungary, where they are very little better than serfs or slaves, that to compel them to inhabit one spot results in any benefit to the race itself.

In Scotland to-day they are often gathered into large communities, as at Yetholm in the Cheviot Hills; the majority, however, as in England, roam over the country for the most

part, and all have retained their freedom and
race characteristics, which seem, save in the
particular of their music, to be lost to those
in Hungary. In England as in America
they wander from city to city, village to village, during the summer, in families and in
communities, practising the same arts that
they practised when they entered Europe
from Asia so many hundred years ago.

To be convinced that the Gypsy is worthy
of attention, and that his race is not a mere
handful of degenerate persons banded into
an association of thieves and vagabonds, as
many ignorantly suppose, it is only necessary
to give a few statistics, not very accurate, I
fear, but as nearly exact as can be obtained
at this time, to show how generally and in
what numbers they are scattered over the
world. In Hungary, where they are known
as *Czijanyok* and *Pharaonepek* — Pharaoh's
people — there are one hundred and forty
thousand; in Transylvania and the Princi-
palities one hundred and sixty-two thousand;
in Spain, where they are called *Zincali* and
Gitanos, there are forty thousand; in England and Scotland, eighteen thousand — this
number has much diminished of late years,

Facts about the Gypsies

owing to the closing of the commons and to emigration to America; in Poland, two thousand; in Russia, ten thousand; in Germany, France, and Italy combined, forty thousand; in Norway, fifteen hundred; and so on till the total number of Gypsies in the world is computed to be about five millions.

SOME HISTORIC GYPSIES

SOME HISTORIC GYPSIES

THERE is little doubt that in the days of the Border wars the Gypsies stole cows with great impartiality from both English and Scotch, and that in large bands they even took remote and ill-guarded castles by storm, the unsettled and lawless condition of the times sheltering them to the extent that their crimes were often attributed to more open and less wary foes.

A few words about the famous Caird of Barullion, — Willie Marshal, king of the Gypsies of the West Lowlands. He was born in Kirkmichael Parish in or about the year 1671, and he died at Kirkcudbright on the 23d of November, 1792, in the one hundred and twentieth year of his age. His monument is still shown in the church, decorated with his escutcheon.

Sir Walter Scott says of this worthy, in his introduction to "Guy Mannering," "It cannot be said that this unusually long lease of existence was noted by any particular excellence of conduct or habits of life. Willie had been pressed or enlisted seven times, and had deserted as often, besides three times running away from the naval service." He was seventeen times lawfully married. Sir Walter also tells us a little anecdote of the excellent Willie's earlier years, when he occasionally took an evening walk upon the King's Highway to relieve weary travellers of the weight of their purses. On one of these evening excursions, narrates Sir Walter, Willie, meeting the Laird of Bargally in a lonely spot on the road between Carsphairn and Dalmellington, demanded his purse, but did not obtain it without a severe struggle, in which the laird's bonnet fell into the dust. The bonnet, in the hasty parting, was left where it fell. A respectable farmer happening along soon after the struggle, seeing the bonnet in the dust, and being a canny body and thrifty withal, alighted, and, in the words of Sir Walter, " somewhat imprudently placed the bonnet upon his head." At this moment the Laird of Bargally returned with assistance, and, recognising the bonnet, charged the worthy farmer with the theft and straightway took him into custody. The trial came on before the circuit court in due season, the criminating bonnet lying upon the table before the judge. The Laird of Bargally swore to bonnet and man, and the case seemed gloomy indeed for the prisoner, the judge being prejudiced against him. But at this point there entered the court none other than the Caird of Barullion, who, pushing his way to the bar, caught up the bonnet, and thrusting it down on his brow, looked the laird full in the face, crying out: " Look at me, sir ! and tell me by the oath you have sworn — am I not the man who robbed you between Carsphairn and Dalmellington? " " By heaven ! you are the very man ! " cried the laird.

Whereupon Willie turned and addressed himself to the Court:

" You see what sort of memory this gentleman has ; he swears to the bonnet, whatever the features under it. If you yourself, my lord, will put it on your head, he will be willing to swear that your lordship was the party who robbed him."

It is needless to say that the farmer was set at liberty, and that Willie Marshal was in

nowise inconvenienced by the timely assistance which he lent.

While the king of the Gypsies was thus
laudably occupied, his royal consort, Flora,
contrived, it is said, to steal the hood from
the judge's gown, for which offence, combined with her presumptive guilt as a Gypsy,
she was banished to New England, whence
she never returned.

The last Gypsy queen of Scotland, Esther
Faa, died in 1883, and is buried at Yetholm.
She was a very remarkable woman, and the
story of her fight for her throne, her coronation, and her death, is told by Mr. Edgar
Wakeman, who has spent much time with
the Gypsies in various parts of the world, and
has written much and entertainingly of his
wild friends. He tells how, upon the death
of William Faa, the acknowledged king of
the Scottish Gypsies, his daughters Esther
and Helen fell to quarrelling, each being
ambitious to reign in her father's stead.
Esther based her claim upon the fact that
she was first born ; Helen, hers, that she was
the favourite daughter, and that it was her
father's wish that she should succeed him.
Both were women of remarkable stature,

being each about six feet in height, and of powerful build. Both canvassed the Gypsy camps of Scotland for supporters, and the result of the election could not be foreseen, when the two brawny sisters, unable to longer endure the strain, came to blows. The battle was long and fierce, and Esther was not victorious until she had thoroughly demonstrated her superiority of strength and endurance. From that day forth Helen, who, I believe, still lives at Yetholm, had no desire to rule over her sister's subjects. In due time Esther was crowned with great ceremony. She died at Kilso, and her funeral cortège, Mr. Wakeman tells us, from Kilso to Kirk-Yetholm, was a memorable one. Besides hundreds of her race, thousands came to Yetholm. Upon her coffin lay the royal cloak of red; upon that a great wreath of white roses. Both were buried with the queen. The crowd about the grave was so vast that the clergyman found it impossible to press through the throng to say a few words over the body. The grief of the Gypsies was unmeasured.

So recently in England as 1878, Queen Victoria was welcomed to Dunbar by a

Gypsy queen. The Gypsy was dressed in a black robe with white silk trimmings, and about her shoulders was a yellow handkerchief. Behind her stood two other women, one of them noticeable for her rich gown of purple velvet, and two stalwart men conspicuous by their scarlet coats.

In America Matilda Stanley was recognised as queen of the Gypsies, and was given, upon her death in 1878, a royal burial at Dayton, Ohio, Gypsies coming from the most distant parts of the country to be present at the obsequies. In the following year another queen was elected at Dayton, — Matilda II., — who is, I believe, travelling the roads and telling fortunes at this present time.

I knew a niece of the late queen very well, and have often heard her speak of her aunt with singular respect. She took great pride in the relationship. As a rule, however, the Gypsies are almost entirely self-governing, and resent now, as they did in the olden time when good King James ordered his sheriffs to assist Johnnie Faw, lord and earl of Little Egypt, to control his subjects, any attempt that may be made to rule them, or even to direct their movements. One can hardly meet with a band of rovers without finding Pharaohs among the men, and in the oldest woman one is sure to meet a Queen of Egypt. Strange as it may seem, the very number of these sovereigns, far from indicating a much-governed people, is the surest proof of their democracy.

TRAITS AND
CHARACTERISTICS

TRAITS AND CHARACTERISTICS

A S the hearth is the heart of the house-
home, so the Sarshta is the heart of
the tent-home. The Gypsies do not, as many
suppose, use the tripod from which to hang
the kettle, but instead use a piece of iron
resembling somewhat a short crowbar with
one end sharpened and the other twisted to
form a hook. The sharp end is driven into
the ground at an angle that leaves the hook
above the fire, and on this hook the kettle
is hung.

The characteristic tent of the race is, in
America at least, seen no more. It was
usually formed of brown blankets, these being
thrown sometimes over the wagon tops, or
supported by poles. These tents were always low and usually small; but the tents
one now sees in America are frequently of
generous size, often gaudy with red stripes,
and almost invariably made of heavy canvas. The wagons, or vans, are usually costly

19   289

and showy, a plain van costing six or seven hundred dollars, and an elaborate one from one to several thousand. When travelling and making but brief halts the Gypsies sleep in their wagons, though a tent is pitched for shelter and comfort.

I have seen Gypsy beds that were inviting, and clean and soft too, with mattress and feathers, and gay with wonderful quilts. Chairs are not often met with, for the obvious reason that they are troublesome and not easily packed away when a family is travelling. In the place of chairs there is always the clean straw to sit on, and the bedding makes an impromptu divan when rolled up and covered with blankets. Boxes or trunks hold the family treasures and wardrobe, and it is a treat to get a glimpse of their contents. Often fine shawls, gowns of silk, even cloaks of sealskin, find their way thither; bright kerchiefs there are sure to be, and strange apparel in which the Rommany ranis — Gypsy ladies — array themselves, as they say, " Gypsy fassion." Jewels there are, — fine corals, strings of amber beads, pearls, and I have seen diamonds appear from beneath some old cloak or gown to glitter for friendly admiration in the light of the camp-fire. The rings and earrings and brooches of gold that the women affect are very different in pattern and make from those worn by the " Gorgios " — all who are not Gypsies — and often much prettier. There is a custom among them of burning the clothes of the dead. Were this not the case many rare heirlooms would descend from generation to generation.

The romance which they impress others as possessing, with which they have always impressed those who studied or knew them, — and upon which they constantly trade, — is real and a part of them, but it is too intangible for pencil or camera. The red cloak and the huge bonnet of beaver are now rarely met with, though in past days, early in this century, it was the distinctive dress of the women. The men still affect corduroys, gay waistcoats, and gaudy buttons, and both men and women possess the faculty of making the most indifferent garb picturesque and attractive.

I have once in a while met with these people when their possessions were few. I remember having a talk by the roadside with a Gypsy who seemed to possess very little of this world's goods, even in a portable form. There were two old horses, a miserable wagon, — the cover mended and darned, — no tent, only a few blankets on the straw for a bed, and no clothes to exchange for those that he wore on his back. He was a generally bad character, as I could see by the one eye that observed me while the other looked off to the woods. His wife was old and her face was marked by the smallpox; she was stout and coarse, and squalid withal, and as fearful a creature as I ever beheld; but in her eyes was the witch-look, and I know that she could tell a good fortune. They had met with bad luck, and seemed the pariahs of their race. I stood in the road watching them till the van went over the hill out of sight, wondering where they had come from and where they were going.

A Gypsy will beg most persistently, will even commit petty theft, will always outwit you in a bargain or trade, and be not over-honest generally in his dealings with those outside his own race; but the Gypsy rarely or never commits a heinous crime. So true

is this that it may be asserted that the rare
exception proves the rule.

The crimes of the tramp are frequently
laid at the door of the Gypsy, but it should
be understood that there is a vast difference
between them. The tramp has no family,
no home, no belongings, no laws or traditions, to check or control him, while the
Gypsy is most essentially a man with a
family, a lover of his tent-home, ready to
fight for his van and his horses, with a
thousand unwritten laws and traditions hedg-
ing him in. The Gypsy loves his wife and
his children, and is contented and happy:
the tramp, with none of these ties, knows
but one check, — fear of the law.

It is amazing in what seasons the Gypsies
will travel. I have known them to start
from New England homes early in February,
and travel persistently through the snows and
rains and winds, coming hundreds of miles
on their way before the spring overtook them.
Even mid-winter does not always succeed
in housing them, as a little scrap cut from a
local paper testifies. I quote it in its en-
tirety: "In Holmes County, last week, a
man who wished to become wealthy without

trouble applied to a Gypsy for advice, and was told to bury fifty dollars in gold in a secluded place and go next day and dig it up. He did as he was told, and when he dug found one hundred dollars in gold. He was then told to double the amount and bury it in the same place; this he did, and when he again dug, the whole amount was gone!" When this fell under my notice I knew that my friends were abroad and at their old tricks. "Hokanni boro"—the great trick—is time-honoured; it is practised in every land where the Gypsy is known. I had thought that in America in recent years it was more honoured in the breach than in the observance, but I stand corrected. It was for this very trick that an old Rommany dye was burned at the stake in Tennessee many years ago.

When the Gypsies can, they go into the cities as the winter comes on. Here they meet their friends and the time passes merrily enough, the men still trading horses, the women telling fortunes in museums and cheap theatres; but I will repeat the words of a Gypsy friend of mine on this subject:

"What does I when housing in the long

winters? I dresses myself in Rommany fassion and I visits about with my friends and relations, such as may be staying in the same town. I does this for my pleasure and for my recreations. And to keep my hand in and earn a few shillings, I advertises myself in the papers to tell the past, the present, and the future, by the planets, the features, and the lines on the hand. And I generally does a good business."

The Gypsies' chief means of livelihood consist, in America, of fortune-telling and horse-trading. Sometimes the peddling of small articles from door to door is carried on by the women as an adjunct to fortune-telling, and the men are oftentimes handy at small crafts and capable workers in metal. However, these latter and minor means of subsistence are not frequently required in this country, the two principal occupations proving, as a rule, sufficiently remunerative.

Gypsy mothers have always told fortunes and have always been pretenders to forbidden knowledge since the days of their entrance into Europe.

How much they do or do not believe in their power to peer into the mysterious

silence of the past and the darker veil of
the future it is impossible to say; but that
they have no belief whatsoever in their own
power, as has been asserted, seems to be
neither true nor reasonable. There are
times when an old mother in Rom seems
little less than inspired, and will startle the
most sceptical by her divination — times when
yesterday thrills with the life of the present,
when the years that have faded to mean-
ingless dates are flooded with daylight, and
faces all but forgotten frown and smile as of
old, and lips that are now grey-bearded, or
silent, babble and prattle of childish joys.
Perhaps one dreams this, perhaps sees it all
in the glittering eye of the sorceress, or it
may be that the breath of the sweet wind
blowing over summer fields brings some old
perfume or fragrance, waking the scenes
with its subtle suggestions; or it may be the
drowsy charm of the hot sun, or the smoke
of the slow smouldering fire : who can tell?

For the most part the so-called " fortunes " are a mere rigmarole helped out by
keen and highly developed powers of obser-
vation and insight. If the Gypsy thinks
herself but a poor fraud — which no Gypsy

mother will admit — she at least believes that others may possess the faculty to which she pretends. It is by no means unusual to hear an old dye — mother — if she be ailing, complain loudly that she is *chovihan* — bewitched. Mr. Leland says that they often possess or desire books on astrology, palmistry, or the many associated and minor black arts. This I have met with in my own experience ; for, though the Gypsy cannot read the book, she has implicit confidence in it, — the more implicit perhaps on that account, — and keeps it hid away deep in her trunk and counts it her greatest treasure.

Their earnings as fortune-tellers the Gypsy women contribute as their share to the family resources, and in seasons of want or ill-luck, this is often the only source of income. I have been told, but will not vouch for the correctness of the statement, that as great a sum as five hundred dollars has been paid for a single fortune, when there were added to it certain mysterious incantations and spells ; five, twenty, fifty, and even one hundred dollars are frequently demanded and obtained by these sorceresses for special information concerning things yet to come to pass. Fifty cents is the least generally taken for a fortune, while two dollars is the average required by a self-respecting daughter of Egypt when times are easy. Like the rest of us who have wares to offer, when times are hard the witch takes what she can get, and for a penny will often disclose the spot where incalculable treasure lies concealed.

The men are great lovers and keen judges of horses. Ponies of Shetland and other breeds are often to be found in the camps; they are not for trade, but for the delight of the children, who make playfellows of them, being on as familiar terms with them as with their dogs, learning to ride them well and fearlessly at a very early age.

It is stated, and I believe with truth, that the Gypsy has no religion, and that though he outwardly conforms to the observance of the land in which he sojourns, the faith of his neighbours rests lightly upon him. His irreligion is entirely passive. He worships the out-of-doors and freedom, and his creed is the creed of the fox and the deer. But from this circumstance wrong conclusions are drawn, all manner of evil accusations are brought against him, he is accused of cannibalism, is pronounced totally depraved and hopelessly debauched, and generally vile and filthy, both in habits and person. This is all wrong. There is no more virtuous race in the world, no race so faithful in all domestic relations. The Gypsy is a good son, a good husband, a good father; there are seldom drunkards among them, and of an habitual drunkard I have never heard.

As for cleanliness, as Mr. Wakeman says, every day seems a day of special scouring and cleaning; for the Gypsy is a great bather, and scrupulous as regards the clothing that touches his person. Yet I cannot deny that, after all, there is a look of not over-cleanliness about them. Perhaps this may be accounted for by the fact that all the cooking is done at a smoking camp-fire, and the dress is alternately dragged over the dewy grass and the dusty road, and is frequently in contact with ashes. After all, my Lady of Egypt, and Pharaoh her husband, grooming his horses, have some reason for their untidy raiment.

Perhaps the one characteristic most elo-

quent in praise of the Gypsy is his respect
and reverence for age. The government is
purely patriarchal. If you wish to go twice
to a Gypsy camp, see to it that you win the
approval of the oldest dye. If you do not
succeed in this, it were as well not to revisit
the camp. All bend to the sway of mother
and grandmother. Man and wife seem to
start equals in life, with the man, perhaps, a
little in the lead; but at sixty, or earlier, the
man has learned to yield to his wife, and it is
she who controls the movements of the
entire camp. She never abuses the powers
thus delegated to her, but rules mildly and
well for the benefit of all.

Gypsies are rarely brutal or cruel to
children, or to the animals dependent upon
them. They are lavishly charitable to those
who are poorer than themselves, and hospi-
table and polite. They are not friendly to
strangers unless convinced of their sincerity.
As a result of their way of life many strange
customs flourish among them, unheard of by
the outside world. In one family of my
friends the parents will not sanction the mar-
riage of a daughter, however much they may
secretly connive at such a result. Of course

the opposition is, as it is intended to be, without effect. How general this custom is I do not know, but I know that in this family it is deep-rooted, and founded upon tradition.

Not without interest is their code of signal whistles, certain whistles signifying certain things. One sound indicates that silence is required, another that strangers are coming, a third and loud one, to reach distant ears, commands the return of wanderers to the camp, and a fourth announces the fact that it will be well for the hearer to drop everything and come running, for the sheriff is approaching.

Perhaps of all their odd and strange customs the oddest and strangest and the most purely and characteristically Gypsy is the *patteran.* I never can think of it, never can hear the word, without being impressed by the romance that it implies. A woodsman may blaze his way through the trackless forest, but he leaves the gash on the tree as a sign of his course, while the Gypsy can travel a thousand miles and leave no sign that any eye but a Gypsy's can see, and yet the route he has gone is perfectly plain to

the laggard who follows a day's journey behind. Gypsy has followed Gypsy hundreds
of miles, day after day, guided only by the
patteran — the mark at the cross-roads.
The patteran is sometimes made of a handful of grass, sometimes of a heap of sticks
placed with significance, sometimes of a pile
of loose stones so arranged that they show
the way the wanderers have taken. Different families have usually a different form of
the patteran, but all know and rely upon it.

THE GYPSY LANGUAGE

THE GYPSY LANGUAGE

THE Gypsies, like the birds and all wild things, have a language of their own, which is apart from the language of those among whom they dwell, and which seems, like the wanderers themselves, nearer to the heart of nature than our language or ourselves.

It is all very well to be, as we are, dwellers in houses and students of dictionaries; but it is equally well that the Gypsy is as he is, and that his language is deep and warm and full of the charm of the out-of-door world, the scent of the clover and the ripple of streams and the rush of the wind and the storm. For the Rommany speech is full of all this, and though the Gypsy has few traditions, his rich mother tongue must embalm in each word a thousand associations that thrill in the soul of these children of the tents as an echo of far-off times. The Ganges, the Nile, and the Danube have heard and still hear this old language, and some of the starlight and moonlight and the flow of those old tides and the deeds of those old days haunt the words on Gypsy lips to this day.

Born in India, in that cradle of races and nations, grown old ere it borrowed from Persian and Greek, and sojourned in their lands, old when the world was young, to-day it is heard only on the lips of the tent-people by wood and by river; but if one knows a single word of that language, the bend in the road, the shadow of elms, the silver of willows, the red of the sumach, have a new tale to tell. One can never love that best of all places, the wholesome and fresh out-of-doors, with the fullest love, unless he knows these poor wanderers who, for love of nature and freedom, travel the roads of our land.

When the time comes to silence the songs of the birds, to have an end to the play and chirp of the squirrel on his branch in the wood, then, and not until then, will the fitting time come to drive the red shawl, the bright van, and the laughter and wiles of the Gypsy from the free roads into the crime and the grime of city and workhouse.

As it is, the Gypsies alone lend the charm

of life to the green lanes and white roads. They alone live consistently in the midst of nature, and have time or heart for her beauty. The stage-coach is gone forever; the overland droves and the drover are things of a past generation; the merchant's covered wagon crosses the mountains no more; the highways and byways are abandoned by the old-time traffic, and even the peddler with his pack and his gossip seldom knocks at the farm-house door. We have all abandoned the country save the farmer and the Gypsies.

I have often wondered if a farmer knew how much real content he derived from the nominal annoyance of having a Gypsy camp at his door. He may complain of it and no one will dispute him; he can have all the contempt for the Gypsy condition that will make him content with his own, and they will not care; yet every morning he can look across to the tents and see the bit of bright colour and hear the laughter and strange words, and every evening he can see the slow smoke rise against the pale sky and watch the flame in the dark of the tent shadows, and hear the note of a fiddle and the sound of a voice, and the song will be like the song of the birds that needs no applause, but that sinks deep and is not forgotten.

When one meets a wagon on the road, with a horse secured by a halter following the van, and a quiet dog following the horse, and sees that the driver has a dusky complexion and wild black eyes, and that his wife and children are likewise tawny and dark, one may safely cry " *Sarishan!* " to that driver, and be reasonably sure that he will pull up his horse with a stare if you be not of his own people.

" *Sarishan, miri pal! mishto hom me dikkava tute,*" and if one holds out one's hand boldly it will be seized in a friendly grip, and he of the tawny complexion, with a new light in his eyes, will lean over the wheel and ask, " *Romanis ?* " For you have as good as said to that Gypsy, " How do you do, my brother? I am glad to see you."

And then, if the spot be a shady one, or there be such a spot near at hand, and if it be afternoon and the horses seem fagged and the town is not too far away, likely as not that Gypsy will drive to the side of the road,

The Gypsy Language

and if you are handy at such matters you may
help him pitch the tent; but if you are lazy,
or the walk from the town has been long and
hot, you can sit on the trunk of a fallen tree,
or, better still, on the green grass, and teach
the young Gypsy boys to build the camp-fire
Indian fashion; and they will make no objection to being so taught, though they know
the art better than you who presume to
instruct them. And you will hear the *dye*
[mother] speak to her *chavies* [children]
as she sits in the door of the *tan* [tent], and
you *beshing apray the pus* [sitting upon
the straw] by the *yog* [fire] will *rakker
Rommany* [talk Gypsy] with her *rom* [hus-
band], and among many other things, and
much gossip as to who has been married in
Egypt, and as to the times, you will speak of
the *grys* [horses] and of the *juckle* [dog],
and you will watch the *kikkavi* [kettle] boiling above the *yog*, where it hangs on the
sarshta [fire-iron], and so you will use some
common Gypsy words, and when you have
rakkered [talked] enough of the *Rommany jib*
[Gypsy language] you will say, "*Latcho divvus, pal*" [Good day, friend], and "*Kushto
bok*" [Good luck], and as you walk down

309

the *drom* [road] you will hear the *bittu rackli* [little girl] singing this *gillie* [song], exactly as George Borrow, the Rommany Rye, heard it sung years ago in Old England :

> " The Rommany chie
> And the Rommany chal
> Shall jaw tasaulor
> To drab the baulor
> And dook the gry
> Of the farming rye ; "

which, as Mr. Borrow well knew, was not a very excellent song to be on the lips of any young lady, even upon the lips of this black-eyed witch's daughter, for it signifies that the Gypsy lass and the Gypsy lad will go across to poison the pig and bewitch the horse of the farming gentleman. Certainly the sentiment might be improved ; but as you pause on the bridge over the clear stream and look back to the tent, and the wagon and the little singer, gleefully waving her red scarf over her head and dancing about on the turf by the fire, a smile steals to your lips, and you wave your farewells, quite sure that the child is as innocent as and far happier than the children of towns.

The Gypsy Language

There are but few who give this language of the Gypsy a second thought. I wonder how many know that the Gypsy's is the only race that, without land, government, or religion, without history or writings of any sort whatever, preserves a language of its own, while speaking, for hundreds of years, another with equal fluency? No other race, unless a conquering race, was ever able to preserve its language in a foreign land, and no other race in the history of the world has habitually spoken two languages. The Gypsy is quick to master foreign tongues, learning to speak with ease and grace, without the aid of books or teachers, any language that is much spoken in his hearing.

The Rommany *jib*, or Gypsy language, can be spoken without the use of any English words, and is frequently so spoken by the older Gypsies; however, a mixture of English and Rommany is more generally spoken by the younger ones of a family and by all about the camp-fire. There is no doubt that this results in a jargon, and is not well for the older tongue. But we need not fear, for Mr. Leland tells us that the Gypsy is taking a new lease of life in America, that new vitality has come with new scenes and broader pastures, and that the *jib* of the Gypsy profits by this and is spoken with greater purity by the tent-people here than in England.